Focus on U.S. History:

The Era of Expansion and Reform

Kathy Sammis

J. WESTON
WALCH
PUBLISHER

Portland, Maine

User's Guide
to
Walch Reproducible Books

As part of our general effort to provide educational materials which are as practical and economical as possible, we have designated this publication a "reproducible book." The designation means that purchase of the book includes purchase of the right to limited reproduction of all pages on which this symbol appears:

Here is the basic Walch policy: We grant to individual purchasers of this book the right to make sufficient copies of reproducible pages for use by all students of a single teacher. This permission is limited to a single teacher, and does not apply to entire schools or school systems, so institutions purchasing the book should pass the permission on to a single teacher. Copying of the book or its parts for resale is prohibited.

Any questions regarding this policy or requests to purchase further reproduction rights should be addressed to:

Permissions Editor
J. Weston Walch, Publisher
321 Valley Street • P. O. Box 658
Portland, Maine 04104-0658

1 2 3 4 5 6 7 8 9 10
ISBN 0-8251-3337-8

CONTENTS

UNIT 1. TERRITORIAL EXPANSION

UNIT 2. NATIVE AMERICANS AND THE WESTWARD MOVEMENT

UNIT 3. THE GROWING ECONOMY

UNIT 4. AFRICAN AMERICANS AND THE GROWTH OF SLAVERY

UNIT 5. POLITICS

UNIT 6. REFORM MOVEMENTS AND THE NATIONAL CULTURE

CREDITS

Dover Pictorial Archive:	pages 3, 9, 12, 13, 18, 19, 20, 21, 22, 27, 32, 33, 34, 42, 43, 44, 45, 46, 66, 72, 73, 74, 82, 83, 84, 85, 87, 89
The Collection of the New York Historical Society:	page 5
Arms, Armor, and Battles CD:	page 11
National Museum of American Art, Smithsonian Institution, bequest of Sara Carr Upton:	page 15
Library of Congress, LC-USZ 62:	pages 16, 69
North Wind Picture Archives:	pages 26, 48, 50, 51, 54, 58, 59, 61, 63, 68
Woolaroc Museum, Bartlesville, OK:	page 31
American Textile History Museum, Lowell, MA:	page 47
Civil War Memorabilia CD:	page 53
Carl Brand:	page 55
Art Collection of Nations Bank, St. Louis, MO:	page 76

TO THE TEACHER

The United States experienced dramatic changes in the 60 years from the turn of the nineteenth century to the outbreak of the Civil War. The nation's western boundary moved from the Mississippi River to the Pacific Ocean. The industrial revolution arrived and transformed the economy. The country began to become industrialized, transportation was revolutionized, immigrants arrived in record numbers, and cities grew rapidly. Western farming expanded to a large scale, supported by an increasingly sophisticated market economy. Cotton became king in the South, forcing a great increase in the number of enslaved African-Americans. Politics, too, changed, as Andrew Jackson ushered in the era of the common man and political parties crafted campaigns with a decidedly modern-day flavor. All this change inspired a great burst of reformism as well. In studying this era, students will gain an understanding of how the United States completed its march to the Pacific and how it began changing from the relatively simple nation of the Revolutionary era to a country with the more familiar face of industrialization, urbanization, and interest-group politics. They'll also see the beginnings of social movements aiming at equality that continue in our present-day society.

The reproducible student activities in this book are designed to draw students into that era of expansion and reform, so they develop a rich understanding of the complex changes of those times that began to transform American life. Many activities in this book draw on original source materials. This device makes the experiences and thoughts of the people who lived then and shaped these pivotal events accessible to students. It helps students enter into and experience these events and feel the ways in which actual people experienced and affected contemporary life that became history.

Organization

The student activity topics are divided into units guided by the National Standards for History. Each unit begins with several Student Background Pages that give the most relevant information on that unit's topic. A number of reproducible student activity pages follow, including reading selections from original contemporary sources and a variety of decision-making, comprehension, analytical, comparative, chronological, interpretive, research, mapping and graphing, role-playing, interactive, and interdisciplinary activities.

Each unit includes some Extra Challenge activities to provide enrichment for more advanced or adventurous students. Time line activities remind students of chronology while inviting them into wider descriptive and illustrative areas. Maps are provided—you can make copies as needed for applicable activities.

Each unit is preceded by a Teacher Guide, giving an overview of the unit and its objectives, plus specific teaching information on each student activity.

Lower-level students may have some difficulty with reading the original source documents, which contain some old-fashioned and higher-level words and syntax. You might want to go over some or all original source selections in class to be sure all students have a full comprehension of them.

At the back of this book, you'll find a section titled Answers, Additional Activities, and Assessments. For each unit, we've provided answers for the student activities, a list of suggested additional activities, and at least one assessment vehicle. The resource section gives titles of fiction and nonfiction books that will enrich students' learning and be helpful to you, plus media/computer research and enrichment resources. The glossary is reproducible for students' use.

TO THE STUDENT

 The United States changed a lot between 1800 and 1860. It grew tremendously in physical size. The western boundary moved from the Mississippi River to the Pacific Ocean, a vast area. White settlers poured west with the boundary, hungering for land and the free frontier life.

This expansion had its human costs. Native Americans still lived in the Southeast and Old Northwest. The national government forced them to move to new Indian Territory west of the Mississippi. Then the United States fought a war with Mexico and won a lot of territory in the Southwest, including California. Mexicans who lived in those areas lost their land.

Meanwhile, the national economy was growing quickly too. New technology and inventions brought industry and factories. Families didn't work together at home as much anymore. Immigrants flooded in to fill the new factory jobs and swelled the cities. Roads, canals, and railroads linked the different parts of the country—except the lower South. There, the invention of the cotton gin created a "cotton kingdom" of plantations and smaller farms. The region needed ever-increasing numbers of slaves to support this kingdom.

Politics took on a modern-day look in this era. Political parties waged loud and hard-fought campaigns. Most white men could vote and hold office. People said the day of the "common man" in politics had arrived.

All these changes made some people see that reforms were needed. With enthusiasm and hard work, reform-minded people tackled all kinds of social problems. The toughest problem of all was slavery.

The activities you'll be doing for this course of study will help you better understand this era of expansion and reform. You'll work with maps and graphs. You'll put yourself into the shoes of this era's people, deciding whether to support a war, debating the thorny question of slavery in the new territories, thinking of what to bring along in your pioneer wagon. You'll read what this era's people said when they spoke out about the great issues of the times. You'll hear what slaves had to say about their lives. When you're done, you'll have a better grasp of these years of dramatic change for the United States.

*Focus on U.S. History:
The Era of Expansion and Reform*

Name _____ Date _____

Eastern United States

(for use with Units 1, 2, and 3)

Atlantic Ocean

Gulf of Mexico

Focus on U.S. History:
The Era of Expansion and Reform

Name _____   Date _____

Western United States

(for use with Unit 1)

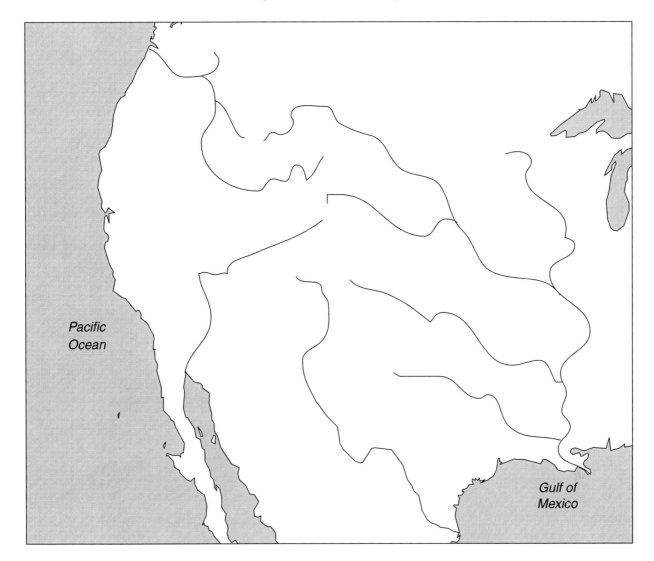

xi   *Focus on U.S. History:*
The Era of Expansion and Reform

Name _____ Date _____

United States

(for use with Unit 1)

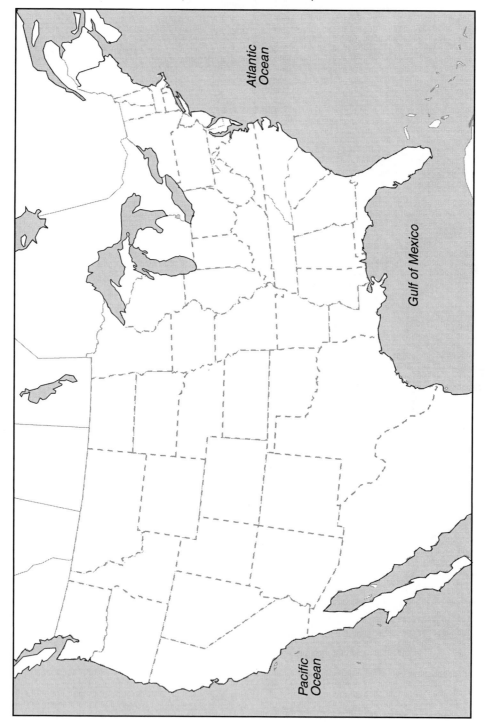

Focus on U.S. History:
The Era of Expansion and Reform

Territorial Expansion

The objectives of this unit are to help students understand the many factors that fueled and, in turn, were fueled by the vast territorial expansion of the United States between 1800 and 1860. Restless colonists had begun the push west almost from the instant they set foot in the New World. They pushed across the Appalachians, then across the Mississippi River, then over the Rocky Mountains, and finally settled up and down the Pacific Coast. They were able to do so because of a series of land acquisitions. In 1803, Napoleon Bonaparte raised money for his European war by selling the Louisiana Territory to the United States. In 1846, the U.S. and Great Britain agreed to split the Oregon Territory at the 49th parallel. Independent Texas joined the Union in 1845. Victory in the war with Mexico in 1848 brought California and New Mexico (most of today's Southwest) into the Union. Settlers poured westward, under the banner of "manifest destiny." The United States was able to do this without interference from Europe, as the War of 1812 brought lasting peace with Great Britain and the Monroe Doctrine announced the nation's policy of prohibiting any new European involvement in the Americas, North or South. This unit's activities are designed to draw students into a better understanding of the territorial expansion of the United States during the first half of the 1800's.

Student Activities

Mapping the Louisiana Purchase uses mapping to make students familiar with the Louisiana Purchase territory and the routes various explorers of the West followed.

Lewis and Clark: The Journals offers students excerpts from the very detailed daily journals that both Lewis and Clark kept as part of the duties of their expedition. The follow-up activity, **Lewis and Clark: The Observations**, has students match the diary entries with specific instructions Thomas Jefferson gave the explorers for making observations. Students learn that the purpose of the expedition was much more than merely trailblazing.

The War of 1812: Causes provides a frame for students to identify causes of the War of 1812, explaining how each pushed the United States toward war with Great Britain.

The War of 1812: Yes or No? has students put themselves into the place of specific American people and then decide whether or not they will support the War of 1812. Part 2 of this activity asks students to map important sites of the war.

Part 1 of **The Monroe Doctrine** presents the main points of the Doctrine as Monroe announced it. Questions guide students to an understanding of the policy Monroe set in his speech. In Part 2 of this activity, students identify the situation in Latin America in 1823 and, from this, explain why that situation prompted President Monroe to declare his doctrine. The Extra Challenge asks students to describe how the United States has applied the Monroe Doctrine in more modern times.

Manifest Destiny presents original source quotes expressing the concept of manifest destiny, the idea that the United States was fated by Providence to expand to the Pacific. Page two of this activity presents manifest destiny as interpreted in artwork. Questions guide students to an understanding of the concept as expressed both in words and in pictures. The Extra Challenge invites students to create their own artistic expression of manifest destiny.

The Mexican War: Raising Volunteers introduces students to the psychology of promoting war. The activity page presents students with a recruiting broadside for the war and asks them to identify the various "hooks" the ad uses to inspire men to volunteer to fight in the war.

The Mexican War: A Chronology Game strengthens students' knowledge of the chronology of events in the Southwest with a game in which students compete to arrange separate events in correct order by date. The Extra Challenge asks them to add actual dates to each event.

The Mexican War: Yes or No? presents quotes from the lively debate in the country about the war. Students use these quotes, plus additional reading, to role-play a debate about whether or not the war with Mexico was justified. Alternatively, students can apply the arguments for and against the Mexican War to a modern-day conflict such as the Vietnam War. This

activity also invites students to debate the concept of "my country, right or wrong" expressed in the quotes.

Mapping the Way West and its follow-up activities give students an idea of the length and complexity of a pioneer journey west. Students start by tracing the trails used by pioneers who went west. The first follow-up activity invites students to read a diary written by an actual pioneer and then contemplate if, after reading such a journal, they would have been willing to take the trip. The second follow-up activity has students apply their mapping and mathematical skills to plan a pioneer trip from Independence, Missouri, to the West Coast.

Making Your Own Way West asks students to put themselves in the place of an emigrant family and decide what items and supplies they will pack in their wagon to bring west with them. Once students have completed their lists, you will present them with a scenario in which they will have to start discarding some of the items they are bringing with them—see the Answer section.

Mapping Territorial Expansion has students create two maps that will show them visually how the United States expanded westward from 1800 to 1853.

Territorial Expansion

The first white colonists in British North America settled along the East Coast. Almost right away, they began pushing westward. By 1804, the United States stretched all the way to the Mississippi River. Then, almost overnight, the United States doubled its territory. Here's how it happened.

The Louisiana Purchase

When Thomas Jefferson became president of the United States, "the West" meant the land between the Appalachian Mountains and the Mississippi River. People in the West depended on the Mississippi for their shipping. The port of New Orleans at the mouth of the river controlled that commerce. The United States wanted New Orleans.

Jefferson

In his first inaugural speech, Jefferson declared that the U.S. had enough land "for a thousand generations." That was in 1801.

Then Spain gave New Orleans back to France. Jefferson didn't want Napoleon Bonaparte to control New Orleans. So he sent a minister to France to offer to buy New Orleans. Napoleon, meanwhile, was gearing up for more warfare in Europe, and he wanted money. So instead of New Orleans, he offered to sell all of the Louisiana Territory to the United States.

Jefferson and his ministers agreed. For $15 million (about 4¢ an acre), the U.S. in 1803 acquired a huge territory stretching from the Mississippi to the Rocky Mountains and beyond. Some people objected, but most agreed that the country couldn't pass up such a bargain. Jefferson soon sent an expedition headed by Meriwether Lewis and William Clark out to explore the vast area. They came back with detailed notes and maps. Along with other pioneer trailblazers, they opened the way for later settlers.

The War of 1812

Soon after he sold Louisiana, Napoleon went back to war with England. This caused all kinds of problems for the United States. French and British warships captured U.S. merchant vessels; the economy suffered badly. The British Royal Navy **impressed** sailors from U.S. ships— they forced these sailors to serve on British ships.

Notable Events of the War of 1812

- The great Indian leader Tecumseh died in battle.
- The attack on Fort McHenry inspired Francis Scott Key to pen "The Star-Spangled Banner," which became the U.S. national anthem.
- Dolley Madison barely escaped from the White House before the British arrived and burned it.

(continued)

Focus on U.S. History:
The Era of Expansion and Reform

Some Americans pressed for war with England. Westerners wanted more territory in the Northwest. Many New Englanders, who depended on shipping, didn't want to tackle the Royal Navy. The War Hawks won out. The war lasted from 1812 to 1815, with the British and the Americans in effect fighting to a standstill. By the time the war was over, Napoleon had been defeated, so shipping was free and open again anyway.

The Monroe Doctrine

Between 1817 and 1822 most of the Latin American countries had become independent from Spain. Other European nations began to show interest in recolonizing them. In answer, President James Monroe declared that from that point on, the American continents were off-limits to Europe. The U.S. would permit no new European colonies in North or South America. This policy later was called the Monroe Doctrine. (The Monroe Doctrine didn't have much effect at first, but it would become important years later.)

Manifest Destiny and Settlement of the West

The U.S. urge to push westward exploded in the 1840's. The nation was prospering, and people felt proud and confident, ready to tackle the pioneering challenge. The population kept expanding because of a high birth rate and a flood of immigration. Settlers poured westward by the thousands. A New York newspaperman, John O'Sullivan, called this movement "**manifest destiny.**" He said the people of the United States were obviously destined—fated—to expand all the way to the Pacific Ocean.

Inspired by manifest destiny (and land hunger), Americans everywhere caught "Oregon fever." During the 1840's, thousands of pioneers made the 2,000-mile trek across the wilderness from Missouri to Oregon. Others trekked to California. The Mormons created their own trail and settled in the Utah wilderness.

Groups started out with packed wagons and high hopes. The trip would prove to be dangerous, exhausting, and seemingly endless. People and livestock died. Treasured possessions lay abandoned along the trail. But still the tide of pioneers went on. When gold was discovered in California in 1848, the tide of emigrants there became a raging flood. So many people flooded in, California was ready to become a state just two years later, in 1850.

The United States: Coast to Coast

James Polk, who became U.S. president in 1845, favored expansion. He had three aims: to make Oregon, Texas, and the Southwest (including California) part of the United States.

(continued)

Focus on U.S. History:
The Era of Expansion and Reform

Here's how he succeeded.

Oregon

- 1840's: Claimed and jointly occupied by Great Britain and the U.S.
- 1845: Polk demands the entire area from Great Britain.
- 1846 Compromise: U.S. and Great Britain sign a treaty dividing Oregon Territory at the 49th parallel (today's boundary).

Texas

- 1820's: Owned by Spain, which invites Anglo settlers in.
- 1836: American settlers rebel, win independence.
- 1845: Texas joins the Union, becomes a U.S. state (slave).
- 1846–48: U.S. fights war with Mexico, wins. Texas remains with U.S.

Southwest

- 1848: U.S. wins Mexican War.
- 1850: California becomes a U.S. state (free).
- 1850: New Mexico and Utah become U.S. territories.

By 1853, the boundaries of the continental United States were set. The expansion across the continent had succeeded.

Ograbme, or the American Snapping Turtle, whose name spelled in reverse is _ _ _ _ _ _ _.

Focus on U.S. History:
The Era of Expansion and Reform

Mapping the Louisiana Purchase

Directions: For this mapping activity, use your map of the western United States.

1. Label the major rivers. Draw in and label the Rocky mountains. Show where the Great Plains are. Also, label these features:

New Orleans	Santa Fe	Fort Mandan	Pike's Peak
St. Louis	Nachitoches	Fort Clatsop	Lemhi Pass
		Fort Adams	

2. Show the following areas on your map:

The Louisiana Purchase	Indiana Territory	Oregon Territory
Orleans Territory	Spanish possessions	

3. Trace the routes of these explorers, and note the dates of their expeditions:

   Lewis and Clark, St. Louis to the Pacific Ocean

   Lewis and Clark, Pacific Ocean to Fort Mandan (two return routes)

   Thomas Freeman

   Zebulon Pike

Extra Challenge: Write in names of major Indian nations and groups along the path of Lewis and Clark.

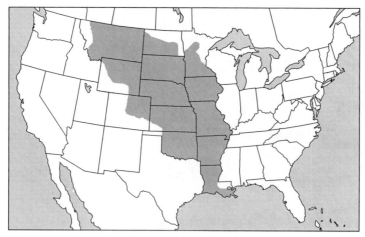

Louisiana Purchase

Lewis and Clark: The Journals

William Clark and Meriwether Lewis led a famous expedition that explored the Louisiana Purchase territory. No white people knew much about it before then. Lewis and Clark both kept detailed journals of their journey. Here are some of their notes.

Lewis (May 11, 1805): About 5 p.m. my attention was struck by one of the party running at a distance towards us and making signs and [hollering] as if in distress.... I immediately turned out with seven of the party in quest of this monster [grizzly bear]....These bears being so hard to die rather intimidates us all; I must confess that I do not like the gentlemen and had rather fight two Indians than one bear; there is no other chance to conquer them by a single shot but by shooting them through the brains.

Lewis (May 17, 1805): Captain Clark narrowly escaped being bitten by a rattlesnake in the course of his walk; the party killed one this evening at our encampment.

Lewis (May 20, 1805): I saw two large owls with remarkable long feathers on the sides of the head which resembled ears.

Clark (May 25, 1805): The country on either side is high, broken, and rocky—a dark brown hard stone intermixed with a soft white sandstone. The hills contain coal or carbonated wood as below and some scattering of pumicestone. The sides of the river are bordered with coarse gravel.

Clark (May 29, 1805): In the last night we were alarmed by a buffalo which swam from the opposite shore ...and went with great force up to the fire where several men were sleeping and was [within] 18 inches of their heads, when one man sitting up alarmed him and he turned his course along the range of the men as they lay, passing between 4 fires and within a few inches of the men's heads.

Lewis (May 29, 1805): I walked on shore and ascended this river about a mile and a half in order to examine it.... The bed was formed of gravel and mud with some sand ...; it was more rapid but equally navigable; there were no large stone[s] or rocks in its bed to obstruct the navigation; the banks were low yet appeared seldom to overflow; the water of this river is clearer much than any we have met with.

Lewis (May 30, 1805): Many circumstances indicate our near approach to a country whose climate differs considerably from that in which we have been for many months. The air of the open country is astonishingly dry as well as pure.

(continued)

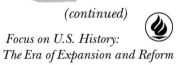

Lewis and Clark: The Journals *(continued)*

Clark (May 31, 1805): The hills and river cliffs of this day exhibit a most romantic appearance. On each side of the river is a white soft sandstone bluff which rises to about half the height of the hills. On top of this cliff is a black earth. In many places this sandstone appears like ancient ruins, some like elegant buildings at a distance, some like towers, etc. and etc.

Lewis (June 26, 1805): The mosquitoes are extremely trouble-some to us.

Lewis (August 10, 1805): I do not believe that the world can furnish an example of a river running to the extent which the Missouri and Jefferson's rivers do through such a mountainous country and at the same time so navigable as they are. If the Columbia furnishes us such another example a communication across the continent by water will be practicable and safe, but this I can scarcely hope.

Lewis (August 19, 1805): [The Indians] are fond of games of risk. They are frank, communicative, fair in dealing, generous with the little they possess, extremely honest, and by no means beggarly. Each individual is his own sovereign master, and acts from the dictates of his own mind; the authority of the chief being nothing more than mere admonition supported by the influence … of his own exemplary conduct.

Clark (August 21, 1805): The women are held more sacred among them than any nation we have seen and appear to have an equal share in all conversation, which is not the case in any other nation I have seen. Their boys and girls are also admitted to speak except in councils. The men wear the hair loose and flowing over their shoulders and face, the women cut short.

Lewis (September 9, 1805): The country in the valley of this river is generally a prairie and from five to six miles wide. The growth is almost altogether pine, principally of the long-leafed kind, with some spruce and a kind of fir resembling the Scotch fir. Near the watercourses we find a small proportion of the narrow leafed cottonwood; some redwood, honeysuckle, and rosebushes form the scant proportion of underbrush to be seen.

Lewis (May 27, 1806): There is a species of whistling squirrel common in these plains which in their habits somewhat resemble those of the Missouri. … These animals form large associations, occupying with their burrows sometimes 20 acres of land. … When you approach a burrow, the squirrels, one or more, usually [sat] erect on these mounds and make a kind of shrill whistling noise. … They do not live on grass as those of the Missouri, but on roots.

*Focus on U.S. History:
The Era of Expansion and Reform*

Lewis and Clark: The Observations

Meriwether Lewis

Directions: Thomas Jefferson sent Lewis and Clark on their exploring trip with specific instructions. They were to make detailed, scientific notes on all of the following. Read the parts of Jefferson's instructions given below. Then record which observations from the Lewis and Clark journal extracts answer which instructions below.

William Clark

1. Explore the Missouri River and its main streams. Take notes about how the river flows between all remarkable points.

2. Take notes on the Native Americans in the areas you go through, noting many details about them and their way of life. (Jefferson added, "In all your intercourse with the natives, treat them in the most friendly and conciliatory manner possible.")

3. Report in detail on the soil and face of the country, and its growth and vegetable production.

4. Report on the animals of the country, especially those not known in the United States.

5. Describe mineral productions of every kind, and salines and mineral waters.

6. Describe the climate in great detail: temperature, rainy and cloudy and clear days, frost, winds, and so on.

The War of 1812: Causes

Part 1 Directions: Describe briefly each item below. Then tell how it helped push the United States toward war with Great Britain.

Tecumseh's confederation, Indian fighting

What: _____

War Cause: _____

Crop prices drop

What: _____

War Cause: _____

Western expansion

What: _____

War Cause: _____

British Orders in Council

What: _____

War Cause: _____

Impressment

What: _____

War Cause: _____

The *Chesapeake* and *Leopard* encounter

What: _____

War Cause: _____

Embargo Act of 1807

What: _____

War Cause: _____

Part 2 Directions: On your map of the eastern United States, mark the movement of British and American forces, the battle sites, and the dates of the battles. Use different symbols for Great Britain and the United States. Also, show the line of the British naval blockade.

The War of 1812: Yes or No?

Directions: Look again at the War of 1812: Causes activity. Then imagine you are each of the people below. Describe how you feel about going to war with Great Britain. Do you support the War of 1812 or not?

1. You are a **white settler** in the Northwest Territory.

2. You are a **merchant shipowner** in Boston.

3. You are a **western farmer** who sells cash crops in New Orleans.

4. You are a **slave-owning rice grower** in Georgia.

5. You are a **Shawnee** living on your nation's grounds in Indiana.

6. You are an **American sailor**.

7. You are a **working-class person** in Philadelphia. Your father fought and died in the Revolutionary War.

8. You are a **Cherokee** living in Tennessee.

The Battle of Lake Erie

11

Focus on U.S. History:
The Era of Expansion and Reform

The Monroe Doctrine

In December of 1823, President James Monroe gave his annual speech to Congress. In it, he stated American policy about the newly independent nations in Latin America. Here are Monroe's main points, which later were called the **Monroe Doctrine**.

That the American continents, by the free and independent condition which they have assumed and maintain, are henceforth not to be considered as subjects for future colonization by any European power.

In the wars of the European powers, in matters relating to themselves, we have never taken any part, nor does it comport with our policy so to do. It is only when our rights are invaded, or seriously menaced, that we resent injuries, or make preparation for our defense.

James Monroe

We should consider any attempt on the part [of the European powers] to extend their system to any portion of this hemisphere as dangerous to our peace and safety. With the existing colonies or dependencies of any European power we have not interfered, and shall not interfere. But, with the governments who have declared their independence, and maintained it, and whose independence we have, on great consideration, and on just principles, acknowledged, we could not view any interposition for the purpose of oppressing them, or controlling in any other manner their destiny by any European power in any other light than as the manifestation of an unfriendly disposition toward the United States.

Part 1 Directions: Answer these questions.

1. What point does Monroe make in the first paragraph of this statement of policy?

   _____

   _____

2. What point does Monroe make in the second paragraph of this statement of policy?

   _____

   _____

3. What point does Monroe make in the third paragraph of this statement of policy?

   _____

   _____

(continued)

The Monroe Doctrine *(continued)*

Part 2 Directions: Find maps of Latin America in 1800 and in 1823.

1. (a) Record here Latin American territories held by European powers in 1800.

   (b) Then, list Latin American nations formed from those territories that had declared their independence by 1823, when Monroe stated his Doctrine.

SPAIN	GREAT BRITAIN	FRANCE	PORTUGAL	NETHERLANDS
Colonies in the Americas—1800				
Independent Latin American nations formed from these colonies by 1823				

2. Using the information you've gathered, explain why President Monroe felt he needed to state his Doctrine.

Extra Challenge: How has the United States applied the Monroe Doctrine in more modern times?

13

Focus on U.S. History:
The Era of Expansion and Reform

Manifest Destiny

White settlers in North America had from the beginning a strong desire to push ever westward. U.S. senators talked about this urge when they debated whether or not to accept the Louisiana Purchase. In 1845, a New York newspaperman named John L. O'Sullivan gave the westward urge/push a name: **manifest destiny**. Read what these people said.

John O'Sullivan, newspaperman (1845)

[Those who oppose the annexation of Texas by the United States have an] avowed object of thwarting our policy and hampering our power, limiting our greatness and checking the fulfillment of our **manifest destiny** to overspread the continent allotted by Providence for the free development of our yearly multiplying millions.

…Texas has been absorbed into the Union in the inevitable fulfillment of the general law which is rolling our population westward;…[it] is too evident to leave us in doubt of the manifest design of Providence in regard to the occupation of this continent.

…In the case of California…the Anglo-Saxon foot is already on its borders. Already the advance guard of the irresistible army of Anglo-Saxon emigration has begun to pour down upon it, armed with the plough and the rifle, and marking its trail with schools and colleges, courts and representative halls, mills and meeting-houses. A population will soon be in actual occupation of California, over which it will be idle for Mexico to dream of domination. They will necessarily become independent.

John Breckinridge, senator from Kentucky (1803)

Why not acquire territory on the west as well as on the east side of the Mississippi? Is the goddess of Liberty restrained by water courses? Is she governed by geographical limits? Is her dominion on this continent confined to the east side of the Mississippi? So far from believing in the doctrine that a republic ought to be confined within narrow limits, I believe, on the contrary, that the more extensive its dominion the more safe and more durable it will be.

Waddy Thompson, minister to Mexico (1846)

That our language and laws are destined to pervade this continent, I regard as more certain than any other event which is in the future. Our race has never yet put its foot upon a soil which it has not only kept but has advanced.…There seems to be a wonderful adaptation of the English people to the purpose of colonization. The English colony of convicts at New South Wales is a more prosperous community than any colony of any other country. That the Indian race of Mexico must recede before us is quite as certain as that that is the destiny of our own Indians.

(continued)

Manifest Destiny *(continued)*

Artists painted the spirit of manifest destiny too. This painting by Emanuel Leutze is titled *Westward the Course of Empire Takes Its Way*. Pictures like this helped fuel "Oregon fever" and other western settlement rushes.

Westward the Course of Empire Takes Its Way, by Emanuel Leutze, 1861

Directions: Answer these questions to gain a better understanding of what "manifest destiny" means.

1. Define the word *manifest*: _____

   Define the word *destiny*: _____

   From this, and O'Sullivan's statement, define the term *manifest destiny*:

   _____

2. What images does Leutze use in his painting to express the idea of manifest destiny? How does he make westward expansion seem strongly appealing to viewers of his painting?

3. What popularly held reasons do O'Sullivan and the others state for expansion across the entire continent?

Extra Challenge: Create your own artistic expression of the concept of manifest destiny. (This could be as seen by Mexicans or Native Americans.)

The Mexican War: Raising Volunteers

Directions: Many of the U.S. soldiers who fought the Mexican War were volunteers. Here's a recruiting ad from New Hampshire. In the spaces provided below, identify the various "hooks"—emotional and psychological appeals—the ad uses to get men to join in the war.

Patriotic appeals:

_____
_____
_____

Appeals to prejudice:

_____
_____
_____

Financial appeal:

_____
_____
_____

State pride appeals:

_____
_____
_____

Appeal to manly courage:

_____
_____
_____

VOLUNTEERS!

Men of the Granite State!
Men of Old Rockingham!! the

strawberry-bed of patriotism, renowned for bravery and devotion to Country, rally at this call. Santa Anna, reeking with the generous confidence and magnanimity of your countrymen, is in arms, eager to plunge his traitor-dagger in their bosoms. To arms, then, and rush to the standard of the fearless and gallant CUSHING---put to the blush the dastardly meanness and rank toryism of Massachusetts. Let the half civilized Mexicans hear the crack of the unerring New Hampshire rifleman, and illustrate on the plains of San Luis Potosi, the fierce, determined, and undaunted bravery that has always characterized her sons.

Col. THEODORE F. ROWE, at No. 31 Daniel-street, is authorized and will enlist men this week for the Massachusetts Regiment of Volunteers. The compensation is $10 per month---$30 in advance. Congress will grant a handsome bounty in money and ONE HUNDRED AND SIXTY ACRES OF LAND.
Portsmouth, Feb. 2. 1847.

Challenge Question: How is the state of Tennessee's nickname related to the Mexican War?

The Mexican War: A Chronology Game

Directions: Cut out each of the boxed events below relating to Texas, the Southwest, and the Mexican War. As quickly as you can, arrange them in correct chronological order. Put the events that occurred earliest at the top of your desk or table. Then line up other events below that one, in the order they occurred over time.

Mexicans adopt a constitution; Mexico becomes a republic.
Texas joins the Union, becoming the 28th U.S. state.
Mexico City, the capital, falls to U.S. forces led by Winfield Scott.
Stephen Austin leads 300 settlers to Texas from Missouri.
Texas forces led by Sam Houston defeat Santa Anna. Texas becomes a republic, an independent nation.
Mexico and the U.S. sign the Treaty of Guadalupe Hidalgo; the U.S. gains New Mexico and California, plus the Rio Grande boundary line for Texas.
Mexico becomes an independent nation, no longer ruled by Spain.
General Zachary Taylor leads U.S. troops into Texas territory that Mexico claims.
Santa Anna's army wipes out American fighters at the Alamo in San Antonio, Texas. Davy Crockett and Jim Bowie die there, along with 200 others.
Spanish explorers claim Mexico, Texas, and California for Spain.
War starts.
Santa Anna, Mexico's ruler, bans Americans from settling in Texas.
U.S. President Polk sends envoy to Mexico, offers to buy Texas, New Mexico, and California (Mexican government refuses to receive the diplomat).
The United States recognizes the new republic of Texas.

Extra Challenge: When you've got your events all lined up, add dates to each one.

Focus on U.S. History:
The Era of Expansion and Reform

The Mexican War: Yes or No?

Going to war with Mexico stirred up a lively debate in the United States. Here are portions of it.

President Polk's war message to Congress (1846)

   Now, after reiterated menaces, Mexico has passed the boundary of the United States, has invaded our territory and shed American blood upon the American soil. She has proclaimed that hostilities have commenced, and that the two nations are now at war.

   As war exists, and, notwithstanding all our efforts to avoid it, exists by the act of Mexico herself, we are called upon by every consideration of duty and patriotism to vindicate with decision the honor, the rights, and the interests of our country.

James Polk

Congressman Abraham Lincoln (1848)

   If the president can show that the soil was ours where the first blood of the war was shed then I am with him for his justification. But if he cannot or will not do this then I shall be fully convinced of what I more than suspect already—that he is deeply conscious of being in the wrong; that he feels the blood of this war … is crying to heaven against him; that originally having some strong motive … to involve the two countries in a war, and trusting to escape scrutiny by fixing the public gaze upon the exceeding brightness of military glory—that attractive rainbow that rises in showers of blood—that serpent's eye that charms to destroy—he plunged into it, and has swept on and on till, disappointed in his calculation of the ease with which Mexico might be subdued, he now finds himself he knows not where.

Senator John M. Berrien (1846)

   The proposition of the senator is that war exists. How does he prove it? Why, by the presence of a Mexican army around the United States army.… I beg to ask how [did the U.S. come to possess that territory]? It was by the march of the United States army into the territory.… If our possession was derived from marching our army there, cannot Mexico exercise the same right? Does priority in an act of hostility vest a national right? The argument of the senator is that the march of the Mexican army was an act of hostility. If so, I have demonstrated that the march of the United States army was an equal act of hostility.

Congressman Columbus Delano (1846)

   We are in the midst of a war which we have engaged in without authority of law and without being in the right, yet now that war has begun, on the principle of "My country, may she be always right, but, right or wrong, my country," I am ready to adopt purely defensive measures.

(continued)

*Focus on U.S. History:
The Era of Expansion and Reform*

The Mexican War: Yes or No? *(continued)*

Senator John J. Crittenden (1846)

I see no reason for the advance of the troops to the Rio Grande. It was not for a moment to be imagined that the angry armies of two angry and quarreling nations should, day after day, face each other with cannons pointed at each other, and only a fordable river between them, and conflict not result. It was conceded that this was disputed territory. What right had the United States to take possession of it? Had not the other disputing claimant an equal right?

Congressman Joshua R. Giddings (1846)

…The President must have known, and we all know, that those military posts were established for the sole purpose of protecting the country, and the sending of our army there must have been done with the moral certainty that war would ensue. The truth is most obvious to the casual reader. The President obviously intended to involve us in war with Mexico.

…It is said, "We must stand by our country." The man who would do otherwise would be unworthy of any country. He only is a true friend of his country who maintains her virtue and her justice; and he is not a true friend to his country who will knowingly support her in doing wrong. Tomorrow this nation will probably be in a state of war with Mexico. It will be an aggressive, unholy, and unjust war. It will then be my duty to use my efforts to restore peace at the earliest practical moment that it can be done on just and honorable principles.

…This war is waged against an unoffending people, without just or adequate cause, for the purposes of conquest; with the design to extend slavery; in violation of the Constitution, against the dictates of justice, of humanity, the sentiments of the age in which we live, and the precepts of the religion we profess.

Senator Thomas Corwin (1847)

What is the territory, Mr. President, which you propose to wrest from Mexico? It is consecrated to the heart of the Mexican by many a well-fought battle with his old Castilian [Spanish] master. His Bunker Hills, and Saratogas, and Yorktowns are there. The Mexican can say, "There I bled for liberty! And shall I surrender that consecrated home of my affections to the Anglo-Saxon invaders?" …'I want room' Sir, look at this pretense of want of room. With twenty millions of people you have about one thousand millions of acres of land inviting settlement by every conceivable argument…. If I were a Mexican I would tell you, "Have you not room in your own country to bury your dead men?"

(continued)

Focus on U.S. History:
The Era of Expansion and Reform

The Mexican War: Yes or No? *(continued)*

General and Senator Samuel Houston (1846)

Was not the crossing of the Rio Grande by the Mexican forces of itself an act of war? Was not the entering our territory by an armed force an act of war? However the decision might hereafter be in regard to the precise extent of our territory, the Mexicans knew full well that the river had been assumed as the boundary. Up to the time of annexation it had been so considered, and, more than that, the Mexicans had never once established a military encampment on the east side of the river.

Congressman Stephen A. Douglas (1846)

A friend of his country in war will feel, speak, and act for his country; will revere his country's cause and hate his country's enemies. America wants no friends, acknowledges the fidelity of no citizen who, after war is declared, condemns the justice of her cause or sympathizes with the enemy.

…The Republic of Texas held the country by a more glorious title than can be traced through the old maps and musty records of Spanish and French courts. She held the country by the same title that our forefathers of the Revolution acquired our territory and achieved the independence of this republic. She held it by virtue of her Declaration of Independence, setting forth the inalienable rights of man.

Congressman John H. Lumpkin (1846)

The boundary of the United States is now extended to the western limit of Texas; her soil is our soil, her people our people; and her resources contribute to our greatness in peace and to our defense in war.

…It is enough for us to know that our soil has been desecrated; that our country has been invaded; that a hostile band of armed soldiers have killed and wounded our citizens; and that the American army, under General Taylor, is in a hazardous situation and in need of assistance.

(continued)

The Mexican War: Yes or No? *(continued)*

Directions:

1. Role-play a debate among supporters and opponents of the Mexican War. Use the readings on these pages as background, and read more of supporters' and opponents' stands on this issue. What is the class consensus—was the war justified or not?

2. Alternatively, or in addition, apply the arguments for and against the Mexican War to a modern-day conflict. One good parallel would be the Vietnam War. Role-play a debate on that war by people of its time. Model your debate on aspects of the Mexican War debate.

3. Discuss or debate the validity of these opposing views: Douglas on "patriotism" versus Giddings on "my country, right or wrong."

Stephen A. Douglas

Joshua R. Giddings

Challenge Question: What famous U.S. writer spent a night in jail because of his opposition to the Mexican War?

Mapping the Way West

Directions: On your map of the western United States, trace these trails, used by pioneers. Use a different color for each trail.

> Old Spanish Trail
>
> Mormon Trail
>
> Santa Fe Trail (including Mountain Route and Cimarron Cutoff)
>
> Oregon Trail (including Sublette's Cutoff)
>
> California Trail
>
> Oxbow Route (Butterfield Overland Mail)
>
> Also, show the South Pass.

Follow-up Activities:

1. Which of the above trails would you have chosen to travel? Find a diary written by someone who actually did go West on that trail in pioneer times. Read her or his account of the trip. If you had read such a diary ahead of time, would you still have wanted to make the journey?

2. Find out how many miles the Oregon or Mormon Trail was, or the route to California via the Oregon and California Trails. How many miles could you expect to go in an average day? How many days and months would your journey take? (Be sure to allow plenty of extra days for accidents, breakdowns, childbirth, and other delays.) When would you have to leave Independence in order to get over the final mountains before they're buried under snow?

Settlers resting along the Oregon Trail

Focus on U.S. History:
The Era of Expansion and Reform

Making Your Own Way West

Directions: You and your family are preparing to head west to California. It is 1845. You'll be traveling by covered wagon. Your family consists of you and your spouse (you're both 22) and your two children, 4 years old and 9 months old. You must make a list of the things you need to take with you on your trip, which may take 5 to 6 months. Divide your supplies into categories. Consult with your spouse and/or other emigrants. You may have read an "emigrant guide" or two, as well.

Food	Tools, utensils	Household goods
Personal items	**Weapons**	**Livestock and their feed**
Things you'll need in Oregon	**Spare wagon parts**	**Special, cherished items you don't want to leave behind**

Mapping Territorial Expansion

For this activity, you will create two maps. Your maps will show how the United States expanded westward from 1800 to 1853.

Map 1 Directions: Use your map of the United States and label it United States—1821. Show the United States and its territories as of 1821. On this map, include the following:

1. States that joined the Union between 1800 and 1821 and their dates of statehood
2. Michigan Territory
3. Missouri Territory
4. Arkansas Territory
5. Mexican territories
6. Oregon Country
7. Florida Territory
8. The borderline established by the Convention of 1818
9. The Transcontinental Treaty line of 1819
10. The Missouri Compromise latitude line of 36° 30'

Map 2 Directions: Use your map of the United States and label it United States—1853. Show how the U.S. and its territories had changed by 1853. On this map, include the following:

1. States that joined the Union between 1822 and 1853 and their dates of statehood
2. Minnesota Territory
3. Unorganized Territory
4. Washington Territory
5. Oregon Territory
6. Utah Territory
7. New Mexico Territory
8. The borderlines established by the Webster-Ashburton Treaty of 1842
9. The border established by the Oregon Compromise of 1846
10. The border established by the Treaty of Guadalupe Hidalgo of 1848
11. The area added by the Gadsden Purchase of 1853

Native Americans and the Westward Movement

The objectives of this unit are to help students understand federal and state policies toward Native Americans during the whites' push to the Mississippi River and to understand the Indians' responses to those policies. In the early 1800's, federal policy was to assimilate Native Americans, to try to persuade Indian peoples to adopt white ways and take up farming, rather than roam vast tracts of land in search of game. The Shawnee chief Tecumseh assembled a great confederacy to fight assimilation and the taking of Indian lands, but the fight failed. Andrew Jackson, elected president in 1828, favored a new policy: removal. He vigorously put into effect the Indian Removal Act of 1830, which decreed that eastern Native Americans could be removed to lands west of the Mississippi River. The Black Hawk and Seminole Wars were the violent responses of some Native Americans to removal. Others, notably the Cherokee, who had assimilated thoroughly, tried to resist removal nonviolently. All failed, and were forced to resettle in Indian Territory. This unit's activities are designed to draw students into a better understanding of these developments in the history of white/Native American relations.

Student Activities

Mapping Native American Removals uses mapping to show students visually the original and relocated territories of eastern Native American peoples. The Extra Challenge asks students to compare the geography of one Native American group's original lands with the resettlement lands.

Two Presidents and Their Policies presents students with quotes from Thomas Jefferson and Andrew Jackson stating their assimilation versus removal policies. Questions guide students to comprehension of the policies, the reasons behind them, and the differences between them. The Extra Challenge asks students for the responses of the southeastern Indians (Creeks, Choctaws, Cherokees, Chickasaws, Seminoles) to Jackson's removal policy.

The Trail of Tears offers students Alexis de Tocqueville's description of the hardships of the trek from the Southeast to Indian Territory. From this, and other readings, students will develop a narrative or write a diary describing one person's experiences during the removal to the West.

Land Hunger presents original source quotes in which white people state why they have a "right" to take Native American lands. From this, students will identify the factors that supposedly gave white people a right to these lands. They will then develop a Native American response to the white people's reasoning.

Native American Responses gives thumbnail sketches of various Native American leaders and presents their words in response to white pressures for their lands. The follow-up, **Native American Responses—An Activity**, uses questions to guide students to an understanding of the different policies counseled by different leaders. The Extra Challenge activity invites students to role-play a tribal council debate on removal and to do further research into the life of one of the Native American leaders quoted.

Native Americans and the Westward Movement

From the earliest days of the colonies, white settlers pushing west had moved into Native American territories. The Indian people tried to hold onto their lands, or at least some of them. But always, the ever-increasing whites won out. Native American groups disappeared or moved farther west themselves.

In the first half of the 1800's, whites were busy filling up the lands east of the Mississippi River. Many Native Americans still lived there.

Indiana Territory, Ohio, Kentucky

Home to: Shawnee, Miami, Potawatomi, Wyandot, Ottawa, Winnebago, Sauk and Fox, Kickapoo

Southeast

Home to: Cherokee, Creek, Choctaw, Chickasaw, Seminole

U.S. Policy: Assimilate (Live Like Whites)

In the early 1800's, most U.S. political leaders favored a policy of getting Native Americans to adopt white ways. The Indians would stay on (part of) their lands and became farmers rather than hunters. Most Native Americans weren't interested in this.

Tecumseh, a Shawnee chief, rejected assimilation. He traveled from the old Northwest to the Southeast, gathering tribes into a great union. He and his brother Tenskwatawa, the Prophet, told their people to reject white ways and fight for their land. Their efforts failed at the Battle of Tippecanoe, when their village headquarters was destroyed.

U.S. Policy: Removal

In defiance of U.S. government policy, white settlers and state leaders kept pushing for Indian lands. A new U.S. policy arose, favored by President Andrew Jackson: **removal**. He vigorously put into effect the Indian Removal Act of 1830. This law said Native Americans could be removed from their lands east of the Mississippi. They would resettle west of the big river in Indian Territory, on land set aside for them by the federal government. Whites and Indians would live apart and that would solve the problems.

Speckled Snake, Creek:

Brothers! I have listened to a great many talks from our great father. But they always began and ended in this: "Get a little further; you are too near me."

(continued)

Armed Resistance

Some Native American groups fought removal, literally.

Black Hawk led his Sauk and Fox people in armed resistance to the removal policy. The Black Hawk War flared up and was snuffed out in Wisconsin and Illinois in 1832.

Osceola led his Seminoles in Florida in an armed resistance called the **Second Seminole War**. The Seminoles fought guerrilla-style from the swamps, continuing their resistance after Osceola's death in 1838. They evaded U.S. Army attempts to move them from 1835 until 1842. Eventually, most Seminoles agreed to go west. Some, though, stayed hidden in the Florida swamps.

Osceola

Peaceful Resistance: The Cherokee

When the U.S. government pushed assimilation, the Cherokee in the Southeast did adapt themselves to live like whites. They had prosper-ous farms, orchards, and cattle herds. **Sequoyah** invented a Cherokee alphabet; soon there was a Cherokee newspaper.

Sequoyah

Living peacefully like whites did the Cherokee no good. They drew up a constitution and tried to establish their own nation. The Supreme Court agreed the Cherokee had a right to rule their own land. But President Jackson wouldn't enforce the court's decree.

President Andrew Jackson

Finally, the Cherokee had to leave for Indian Territory. Their sad journey is called the **Trail of Tears**. Up to 4,000 Cherokee died on the way west. The Creek, Choctaw, and Chickasaw, too, made this sad and deadly journey.

Mapping Native American Removals

In the mid-1800's, Andrew Jackson established a policy of removing eastern Indians from their traditional lands. They were forced to move to "Indian Territory" west of the Mississippi River.

Directions: On your map of the eastern United States, do the following:

1. Label the general areas inhabited by:

Cherokee	Creek	Choctaw	Miami
Chickasaw	Seminole	Shawnee	Wyandot
Potawatomi	Winnebago	Sauk and Fox	

2. Locate and label:

Springfield, Missouri
New Echota, Georgia
Vicksburg, Mississippi
Nashville, Tennessee
Memphis, Tennessee
Indian Territory
Mississippi River
Arkansas River
Ohio River
Red River

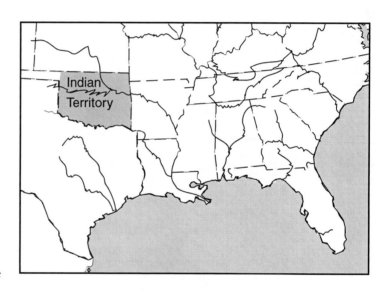

3. Draw lines showing the general relocation routes of the Native American groups. Calculate the rough approximate length of each route.

Extra Challenge: You can do this activity individually or as a member of a small group. Choose one of the Native American groups on the map. Compare the geography of that group's original lands (the ones they were removed from) with the resettlement lands. Consider factors such as topography, climate, soil and vegetation, and natural resources. Present your findings in chart form. Then make a general conclusion: How well prepared would your Native American group be for life in the resettlement area, based on what they were used to in their original lands? How did they actually readjust?

Two Presidents and Their Policies

Federal policy toward Native Americans changed during the 1800's. Thomas Jefferson promoted farming for the Indians on their traditional lands in the early 1800's. Andrew Jackson became president in 1829. His ideas for the southeastern Native Americans were quite different. Read what these two presidents had to say.

Thomas Jefferson (1802–1803)

To assembled Native Americans: We shall, with great pleasure, see your people become disposed to cultivate the earth, to raise herds of the useful animals, and to spin and weave, for their food and clothing. These resources are certain; they will never disappoint you: while those of hunting may fail, and expose your women and children to the miseries of hunger and cold. We will with pleasure furnish you with implements for the most necessary arts, and with persons who may instruct you how to make and use them.

To Congress: [We will] multiply trading houses among [the Indians], and place within their reach those things which will contribute more to their domestic comfort than the possession of extensive but uncultivated wilds. Experience and reflection will develop to them the wisdom of exchanging what they can spare and we want for what we can spare and they want.

Andrew Jackson (1829)

I informed the Indians inhabiting parts of Georgia and Alabama that their attempt to establish an independent government would not be countenanced by the Executive of the United States, and advised them to emigrate beyond the Mississippi or submit to the laws of those states.

…Surrounded by the whites with their arts of civilization, which by destroying the resources of the savage doom him to weakness and decay, the fate of the Mohegan, the Narragansett, and the Delaware is fast overtaking the Choctaw, the Cherokee, and the Creek. That this fate surely awaits them if they remain within the limits of the states does not admit of a doubt. Humanity and national honor demand that every effort should be made to avert so great a calamity. It is too late to inquire whether it was just in the United States to include them and their territory within the bounds of new states, whose limits they could control. That step can not be retraced.

…It seems to me visionary to suppose that in this state of things claims can be allowed on tracts of country on which [the southeastern Indians] have neither dwelt nor made improvements, merely because they have seen them from the mountain or passed them in the chase. Submitting to the laws of the states, and receiving, like other citizens, protection in their persons and property, they will ere long become merged in the mass of our population.

(continued)

Two Presidents and Their Policies *(continued)*

Directions: Answer these questions about Jefferson's and Jackson's policies toward Native Americans.

1. Jefferson wanted Indians to become farmers, rather than hunters, on their traditional lands. How would this benefit the federal government and white people in general?

    _____

    _____

2. Jefferson also wanted federal trading stores to sell manufactured goods to Native Americans. How would this benefit the federal government and white people in general?

    _____

    _____

3. How was Jackson's policy different from Jefferson's? _____

    _____

4. What reasons did Jackson give to justify his policy? _____

    _____

    _____

5. What were the real reasons for Jackson's policy toward the southeastern Indians?

    _____

    _____

    _____

6. What is inaccurate about Jackson's description of the lands claimed by the southeastern Indians? _____

    _____

Extra Challenge: What were the responses of the southeastern Indians to Jackson's removal policy?

Focus on U.S. History:
The Era of Expansion and Reform

Name _____

Date _____

The Trail of Tears

President Andrew Jackson made removal of Native Americans from the Southeast to west of the Mississippi River seem desirable. It would be a smooth journey aided by the U.S. government:

> To these districts [west of the Mississippi] the Indians are removed at the expense of the United States, and with certain supplies of clothing, arms, ammunition, and other indispensable articles; they are also furnished gratuitously with provisions for the period of a year after their arrival at their new homes.

Here's what the actual trip was like, as witnessed by a French traveler and author named Alexis de Tocqueville:

> At the end of the year 1831, while I was on the left bank of the Mississippi, … there arrived a numerous band of Choctaws…. [They] had left their country and were endeavoring to gain the right bank of the Mississippi, where they hoped to find an asylum that had been promised them by the American government. It was then the middle of winter, and cold was unusually severe; the snow had frozen hard upon the ground, and the river was drifting huge masses of ice. The Indians had their families with them, and they brought in their train the wounded and the sick, with children newly born and old men upon the verge of death. They possessed neither tents nor wagons, but only their arms and some provisions. I saw them embark to pass the mighty river, and never will that solemn spectacle fade from my memory. No cry, no sob, was heard among the assembled crowd; all were silent.

Directions: Read more about the removal of the southeastern Indians. Then develop a narrative, or write a diary, that tells the story of one person's experiences during the removal to the West.

The Trail of Tears,
by artist
Robert Lindneux

Land Hunger

White people gave various reasons why they had a "right" to Native American lands. Here are some.

James Fenimore Cooper (1828)

That neither the United States, nor any individual state has ever taken possession of any land that, by usage or construction, might be decreed the property of the Indians, without a treaty and a purchase, is, I believe, certain. How far an equivalent is given, is another question: though I fancy that these bargains are quite as just as any that are ever driven between the weak and the strong, the intelligent and the ignorant. It is not pretended that the value of the territory gained is paid for; but the purchase is rather a deference to general principles of justice and humanity, than a concession to a right in the Indians, which itself might admit of a thousand legal quibbles.

Cooper

Emmerich de Vattel, Swiss jurist (1760)

The people of Europe, too closely pent up, finding land of which these nations are in no particular want, and of which they make no actual and constant use, may lawfully possess it, and establish colonies there.... The earth belongs to the human race in general, and was designed to furnish it with subsistence; if each nation had resolved from the beginning to appropriate to itself a vast country, that the people might live only by hunting, fishing, and wild fruits, our globe would not be sufficient to maintain a tenth part of its present inhabitants. People have not then deviated from the laws of nature in confining the Indians within narrow limits.

Caleb Atwater, U.S. treaty negotiator (1829)

That such a beautiful country was intended by its Author to be forever in the possession and occupancy of serpents, wild fowls, wild beasts and savages, who derive little benefit from it, no reasonable man can for one moment believe who sees it.

Directions:

1. From what you have read, list the factors that supposedly gave white people a right to take Native American lands.

2. As a member of a small group, develop a Native American response to the white people's reasoning.

Focus on U.S. History:
The Era of Expansion and Reform

Native American Responses

Native American leaders suggested various ways of dealing with white pressures for their lands. Here are some.

Tecumseh *was a powerful Shawnee chief and orator. He organized many of the Native American tribes east of the Mississippi River in a great confederation to drive the whites off their lands.*

Accursed be the race that has seized on our country and made women of our warriors.... Let the white race perish. They seize your land, they corrupt your women, they trample on the ashes of your dead! Back whence they came, upon a trail of blood, they must be driven!

Sagoyewathat (Red Jacket) *was a Seneca chief and powerful orator who spoke against white attempts to convert the Indians to Christianity.*

Brothers, our seats were once large and yours were small. You have now become a great people, and we have scarcely a place left to spread our blankets. You have got our country but are not satisfied; you want to force your religion upon us.

Brothers, you say there is but one way to worship and serve the Great Spirit. If there is but one religion, why do you white people differ so much about it?

Brothers ... we are told that your religion was given to your forefathers and has been handed down from father to son. We also have a religion which was given to our forefathers and has been handed down to us, their children.... The Great Spirit does right. He knows what is best for His children; we are satisfied.

Brothers, we are told that you have been preaching to the white people in this place. These people are our neighbors. We are acquainted with them. We will wait a little while and see what effect your preaching has upon them. If we find it does them good, makes them honest and less disposed to cheat Indians, we will then consider again of what you have said.

Sagoyewathat

Black Hawk *led the Sauk and Fox against the white settlers who had taken over their Illinois lands in what was called the Black Hawk War of 1832.*

There were no deer in the forest. The opossum and beaver were fled; the springs were drying up; our women and children were without food to keep them from starving. The spirit of our fathers arose and spoke to us to avenge our wrongs or die.

(continued)

Native American Responses (continued)

Shabonee *was a peace chief of the Potawatomi who refused to join in Indian wars against white settlers in the Northwest lands.*

In my youthful days, I have seen large herds of buffalo on these prairies, and elk were found in every grove, but they are here no more, having gone towards the setting sun....The red man must leave the land of his youth and find a new home in the far west. The armies of the whites are without number, like the sands of the sea, and ruin will follow all tribes that go to war with them.

Osceola *led his Seminole people in the Second Seminole War in Florida. They fought against being removed to the Indian territory west of the Mississippi.*

My Brothers! The white people got some of our chiefs to sign a paper to give our lands to them, but our chiefs did not do as we told them to do; they did wrong; we must do right....

My Brothers! When the Great Spirit tells me to go with the white man, I go; but he tells me not to go. The white man says I shall go, and he will send people to make me go; but I have a rifle, and I have some powder and some lead. I say, we must not leave our homes and lands.

Osceola

Major Ridge *was a Cherokee leader confronted with the federal government's demand that his people leave their lands and remove to Indian territory west of the Mississippi River.*

I know the Indians have an older title [to this land] than [the whites]. We obtained the land from the living God above. They got their title from the British. Yet they are strong and we are weak. We are few, they are many. We cannot remain here in safety and comfort....We can never forget these homes, I know, but an unbending, iron necessity tells us we must leave them. I would willingly die to preserve them, but any forcible effort to keep them will cost us our lands, our lives and the lives of our children. There is but one path of safety, one road to future existence as a nation....Give up these lands and go over beyond the great Father of Waters.*

* From *Cherokee Tragedy: The Story of the Ridge Family and the Decimation of a People*, by Thurman Wilkins (New York: Macmillan Publishing, 1970).

Native American Responses—An Activity

Directions: After you have read the statements by Native American leaders, answer these questions. You may also do either of the Extra Challenge activities.

1. a. Which leaders counseled armed resistance to white plans?

   _____

   b. Summarize their positions: _____

   _____

   _____

2. What particular type of resistance did Red Jacket advocate? _____

   _____

3. a. Which leaders agreed to give in to white plans? _____

   _____

   b. Summarize their positions: _____

   _____

   _____

4. What arguments do the southeastern Indians make against removal from their lands?

   _____

   _____

   _____

Extra Challenges

5. Role-play a tribal council debate. Some council members favor moving to Indian territory west of the Mississippi River. Others insist they must stay on their traditional grounds east of the Mississippi.

6. Research the life of one of these Native American leaders. Quote more of his words and orations, and describe the outcome of his people's relations with the whites. You could also deliver one of his orations aloud.

The Growing Economy

The objective of this unit is to guide students to an understanding of how the industrial revolution grew and spread, changing Americans' lives in the process and drawing a flood of new immigrants. During the first half of the nineteenth century, technological advances and inventions brought the industrial revolution to the United States. As the economy grew, land and water transportation were transformed as well, with steamboats plying the rivers and canal and railroad networks spreading throughout the North and West. Factory work created a new, unskilled laboring class. It drew women and children, as well as men, away from family-centered, home-based occupations. Cities grew rapidly, many of them populated by poor immigrants. This industrial, urban development, however, occurred mostly in the North and West. The South remained largely rural, a region of cotton plantations and small farms. This unit's activities are designed to draw students into a better understanding of these changes.

Student Activities

Inventions and Inventors challenges students to identify the men who invented or built various devices important to the industrial revolution in the United States and to explain how each device affected the national economy. The Extra Challenge asks students to do some research and tell the full story of the invention or development of one of these devices.

Getting from Here to There shows students various nineteenth-century means of transportation. Students are asked to identify each, tell where it was generally used and what it was used for, and what its advantages and disadvantages were.

Mapping the New Travel Routes uses mapping to show students visually how the canal, railroad, and improved road network spread across the United States—and largely bypassed the South. The Extra Challenge asks students to describe their trip in the mid-1800's on a railroad, canal, or national road.

Traveling the United States presents two vivid, funny descriptions of travel in the U.S. written by British visitors Fanny Kemble and Charles Dickens.

Students should enjoy the excerpts and can use them as background for the Extra Challenge activity in Mapping the New Travel Routes.

Mill Life presents a timetable for the Lowell Mills, which shows students what a long day, with few breaks, mill workers of the mid-1800's put in. Students put themselves in the place of a mill worker and use the timetable to write journal entries describing several typical days at the mill.

The Industrial Revolution and You puts students into the place of specific Americans and has them tell how the industrial revolution has affected their lives.

A Tide of Immigration presents students with a graph of immigration to the United States from 1800 to 1866. **Reading the Immigration Graph** helps students interpret the graph by answering a series of questions. The Extra Challenge asks students to construct a graph showing immigration as a percentage of the total U.S. population during the years from 1800 to 1865. (Population figures are available in *Historical Statistics of the United States*.)

Coming to the United States gives a graphic contemporary description of a shipful of Irish emigrants in steerage. The activity asks students to imagine themselves as one of those emigrants and describe his or her motives, hopes, expectations, and actual experiences.

The Growing Economy

A Revolution in Industry

The **industrial revolution** swept across the United States in the first half of the 1800's. Industry and the factory system sprouted up everywhere. Machines began producing things, like cloth, that people had always made by hand. Other machines made farming much more efficient, like an industry.

Several clever people got things started.

Eli Whitney's cotton gin transformed the economy of the South.	**Whitney's** all-the-same parts for guns began assembly-line manufacturing.	**Samuel Slater** and **F. C. Lowell** smuggled plans for textile machinery from Britain—in their heads!

A Revolution in Transportation

The growing western economy in the Mississippi Valley needed cheap, efficient ways to get goods to market. River transport had a major drawback: Flatboats could float downstream, but they were slow. And it was terribly difficult to get them back upstream. Moving goods west to east wasn't much better. The roads were absolutely dreadful. To answer these problems, major changes were made.

The **Erie Canal** led the boom in canal digging.	**Steamboats** powered their way upstream and down.	**The National Road** led the way in improved road building.
	Railroad lines linking east with west spread out in the 1850's.	

The Rise of Factories

The rise of factories led to many changes in U.S. life. Skilled workers weren't needed as much. An unskilled, laboring class grew. People worked in mills and factory buildings instead of pursuing cottage trades in their homes. Families no longer commonly worked together in family businesses. But people could afford to buy factory-made goods that had been too costly when handmade.

At first, the textile mills relied on women and children for labor. They filled a gap in the labor pool, and they could be paid less. Sometimes, living and working conditions were relatively good. But generally, hours were long, pay was low, and working conditions were dangerous. When factory owners cut pay and ordered work speedups, mill workers staged one of the nation's first labor strikes.

(continued)

Focus on U.S. History:
The Era of Expansion and Reform

The 1830's and 1840's saw a wave of immigration into the United States. Many of these newcomers found factory jobs. The poorer ones settled in eastern cities, where they competed for jobs with people already there.

Regional Patterns

If you put all this economic expansion on a map, you'd notice some differences among the nation's regions. Railroad lines ran mostly through the North and the West. Most large cities were located in these two regions, too. Most factories were in the North. The West concentrated on agricultural activities: large farms, meat and food processing, and production of farm machinery. The South remained rural, a region of cotton plantations and small farms. All this would spell trouble for the South when the Civil War arrived.

Inventions and Inventors

Directions: Clever people who thought up new machines and processes got the industrial revolution going in the United States. For each device named below,

   1. Identify its inventor or builder (their names make a border around the frame);

   2. Tell how the device affected the national economy.

JOHN DEERE   FRANCIS CABOT LOWELL

Thread-spinning mill Builder: Impact:	**Steamboat (first successful)** Builder: Impact:	**Cotton gin** Inventor: Impact:
Telegraph Inventor: Impact:	**Metal plow** Inventor: Impact:	**Mechanical reaper** Inventor: Impact:
Power loom for mills Builder: Impact:	**Sewing machine** Inventor: Impact:	**Vulcanized rubber** Inventor: Impact:

ELI WHITNEY · ELIAS HOWE · CYRUS McCORMICK (left border)

SAMUEL F. B. MORSE · ROBERT FULTON (right border)

CHARLES GOODYEAR   SAMUEL SLATER

Extra Challenge: Do some research. Tell the full story of how one of these inventions came into being.

41

Focus on U.S. History:
The Era of Expansion and Reform

Getting from Here to There

Directions: The bustling nation and its booming economy needed quick, cheap ways of moving people and goods around. Name each means of transportation pictured below. Then tell where it was generally used and what it was used for. Also tell briefly what the advantages and disadvantages of each were.

1.	What: Where used: Used for: Advantages: Disadvantages:

2.	What: Where used: Used for: Advantages: Disadvantages:

3.	What: Where used: Used for: Advantages: Disadvantages:

(continued)

Getting from Here to There *(continued)*

4. 	What: Where used: Used for: Advantages: Disadvantages:

5. 	What: Where used: Used for: Advantages: Disadvantages:

Challenge Question: Try to find information and illustrations about the following additional means of transportation: **flatboat**, **canal barge**, and **iron steamship**. Identify advantages and disadvantages of each.

Mapping the New Travel Routes

Directions: The need for quick, cheap transportation produced new answers: canals and railroads. Roads were improved, too. On your map of the eastern United States, show the following.

1. **Canals:**

   Erie
   Champlain
   Ohio and Erie

   Miami and Ohio
   Wabash and Erie

2. **Railroads:**

   Erie
   Baltimore and Ohio
   New York Central

   Pennsylvania
   Illinois Central

3. **Roads:**

   Boston Post Road
   Valley Turnpike
   Natchez Trace
   New York–St. Augustine road

   Wilderness Road
   National Road
   other major roads

Challenge Question: Do these transportation systems seem evenly spread out across all the regions of the United States?

Extra Challenge: Describe your trip in the mid-1800's on a railroad, canal, or national road. You're traveling in one of the vehicles from the Getting from Here to There activity. You can draw on the descriptions in the Traveling the United States pages to help imagine what your trip might be like.

Traveling the United States

What exactly was it like traveling through the United States in the 1830's and 1840's? Two English visitors wrote vividly about their experiences.

Frances Anne (Fanny) Kemble, English actress on the road

On stagecoaches: Oh, these coaches! English eye hath not seen, English ear hath not heard, nor hath it entered into the heart of Englishman to conceive the surpassing clumsiness and wretchedness of these leathern inconveniences....

On roads: Away wallopped the four horses, trotting with their front, and galloping with their hind legs: and away went we after them, bumping, thumping, jumping, jolting, shaking, tossing and tumbling, over the wickedest road, I do think, the cruellest, hard-heartedest road, that ever wheel rumbled upon. Through bog and marsh, and ruts, wider and deeper than any Christian ruts I ever saw, with the roots of trees protruding across our path, their boughs every now and then giving us an affectionate scratch through the windows; and, more than once, a half-demolished trunk or stump lying in the middle of the road lifting us up, and letting us down again, with most awful variations of our poor coach body from its natural position. Bones of me! What a road!

On canals and canal boats: I like traveling by the canal boats very much. Ours was not crowded, and the country through which we passed being delightful, the placid moderate gliding through it, at about four miles and a half an hour, seemed to me infinitely preferable to the noise of wheels, the rumble of a coach, and the jerking of bad roads, for the gain of a mile an hour. The only nuisances are the bridges over the canal, which are so very low, that one is obliged to prostrate oneself on the deck of the boat, to avoid being scraped off it; and this humiliation occurs, upon an average, once every quarter of an hour.

Fanny Kemble

…We sat in the men's cabin until they began making preparations for bed, and then withdrew into a room about twelve feet square, where a whole tribe of women were getting to their beds. Some half undressed, some brushing, some curling, some washing, some already asleep in their narrow cribs, but all within a quarter of an inch of each other: it made one shudder.

(continued)

Focus on U.S. History:
The Era of Expansion and Reform

Traveling the United States *(continued)*

Charles Dickens, famous author, touring the U.S.

On railroads: There is a great deal of jolting, a great deal of noise, a great deal of wall, not much window, a locomotive engine, a shriek, and a bell.

…In the center of the carriage there is usually a stove, fed with charcoal or anthracite coal; which is for the most part red-hot. It is insufferably close; and you see the hot air fluttering between yourself and any other object you may happen to look at, like the ghost of smoke.

…Everybody talks to you, or to anybody else who hits his fancy.…Wherever you are going, you invariably learn that you can't get there without immense difficulty and danger, and that all the great sights are somewhere else.

On river steamboats: I go on board again; open the door of the gentle-men's cabin; and walk in. Somehow or other—from its being so quiet, I suppose—I have taken it into my head that there is nobody there. To my horror and amazement it is full of sleepers in every stage, shape, attitude, and variety of slumber: in the berths, on the chairs, on the floors, on the tables, and particularly round the stove, my detested enemy.

…I am among the [early] risers: for it is easy to feel, without going into fresh air, that the atmosphere of the cabin is vile in the last degree.…The washing and dress-ing apparatus, for the passengers generally, consists of two jack-towels, three small wooden basins, a keg of water and a ladle to serve it out with, six square inches of looking-glass, two ditto ditto of yellow soap, a comb and brush for the head, and nothing for the teeth. Everybody uses the comb and brush, except myself. Everybody stares to see me using my own.

On stagecoaches: They are covered with mud from the roof to the wheel-tire, and have never been cleaned since they were first built.

On roads: The first half mile of the road is over bridges made of loose planks laid across two parallel poles, which tilt up as the wheels roll over them; and IN the river. The river has a clayey bottom and is full of holes, so that half a horse is constantly disappearing unexpectedly, and can't be found again for some time.

But we get past even this, and come to the road itself, which is a series of alternate swamps and gravel-pits.…We come to the [deep] spot, sink down in the mire nearly to the coach windows, tilt on one side at an angle of forty-five degrees, and stick there. The insides scream dismally; the coach stops; the horses flounder.

Mill Life

Below is a timetable for the Lowell Mills. Many young women worked there in the 1820's and 1830's. Then children and immigrants took their place. Is this anything like the schedule most workers keep today? Is it anything like your typical school and workday?

Directions: Imagine you work in the Lowell Mills in the 1800's. Use the timetable to guide you as you write entries in your journal. Describe several typical days at the mill. Remember, mills could be dangerous places to work. (For more background, check out the book *The Mill Girls* by Bernice Selden.)

TIME TABLE OF THE LOWELL MILLS,
To take effect on and after Oct. 21st, 1851.

The Standard time being that of the meridian of Lowell, as shown by the regulator clock of JOSEPH RAYNES, 43 Central Street

	From 1st to 10th inclusive.				From 11th to 20th inclusive.				From 21st to last day of month.			
	1st Bell	2d Bell	3d Bell	Eve. Bell	1st Bell	2d Bell	3d Bell	Eve. Bell	1st Bell	2d Bell	3d Bell	Eve. Bell
January,	5.00	6.00	6.50	*7.30	5.00	6.00	6.50	*7.30	5.00	6.00	6.50	*7.30
February,	4.30	5.30	6.40	*7.30	4.30	5.30	6.25	*7.30	4.30	5.30	6.15	*7.30
March,	5.40	6.00		*7.30	5.20	5.40		*7.30	5.05	5.25		6.35
April,	4.45	5.05		6.45	4.30	4.50		6.55	4.30	4.50		7.00
May,	4.30	4.50		7.00	4.30	4.50		7.00	4.30	4.50		7.00
June,	"	"		"	"	"		"	"	"		"
July,	"	"		"	"	"		"	"	"		"
August,	"	"		"	"	"		"	"	"		"
September,	4.40	5.00		6.45	4.50	5.10		6.30	5.00	5.20		*7.30
October,	5.10	5.30		*7.30	5.20	5.40		*7.30	5.35	5.55		*7.30
November,	4.30	5.30	6.10	*7.30	4.30	5.30	6.20	*7.30	5.00	6.00	6.35	*7.30
December,	5.00	6.00	6.45	*7.30	5.00	6.00	6.50	*7.30	5.00	6.00	6.50	*7.30

* Excepting on Saturdays from Sept. 21st to March 20th inclusive, when it is rung at 20 minutes after sunset.

YARD GATES,
Will be opened at ringing of last morning bell, of meal bells, and of evening bells; and kept open Ten minutes.

MILL GATES.
Commence hoisting Mill Gates, Two minutes before commencing work.

WORK COMMENCES,
At Ten minutes after last morning bell, and at Ten minutes after bell which "rings in" from Meals.

BREAKFAST BELLS.
During March "Ring out".........at....7.30 a. m..........."Ring in" at 8.05 a. m.
April 1st to Sept. 20th inclusive.....at....7.00 " " .... " " at 7.35 " "
Sept. 21st to Oct. 31st inclusive.....at....7.30 " " .... " " at 8.05 " "
Remainder of year work commences after Breakfast.

DINNER BELLS.
"Ring out"...... ....12.30 p. m........."Ring in".... 1.05 p. m.

In all cases, the *first* stroke of the bell is considered as marking the time.

The Industrial Revolution and You

Directions: Changes in technology and transportation affected the lives of many Americans. Imagine you are each of the people described below. Tell in that person's words how the industrial revolution in the United States is affecting your life.

1. You are a **young woman**, age 19, unmarried. You live at home on the family farm in New Hampshire.

2. You are a **skilled weaver**. You weave cloth at home on a hand loom.

3. You are a **wheat farmer** in Illinois.

4. You are an **African-American slave** in Virginia.

5. You are **nine years old**, one of seven children in a family that has just arrived in Rhode Island from your native Ireland.

6. You are a **skilled gunsmith**. You make fine guns, one at a time. You also are an expert at repairing guns.

7. You own a **tidewater plantation** in the South.

8. You run a **small shoemaking business** near Chicago.

Factory workers at a Lowell, Massachusetts, mill

Focus on U.S. History:
The Era of Expansion and Reform

A Tide of Immigration

Graph: Immigration to the United States, 1800–1866

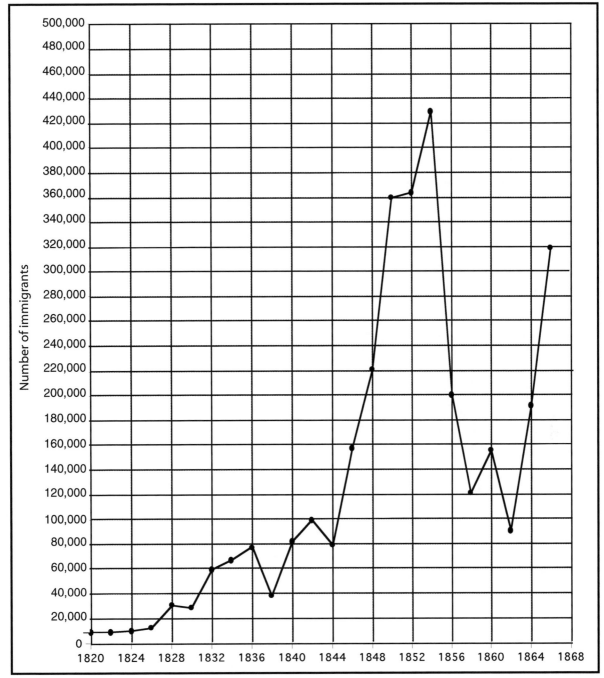

Name _____

Date _____

Reading the Immigration Graph

Directions: Use the information on the immigration graph to answer these questions.

1. a. Did immigration to the United States increase every year during this period?

    _____

    b. Overall, did the United States experience a steady increase in immigration in the years up to 1854? _____

2. Why might immigration from Europe have started to pick up after 1815?

    _____

3. a. When during the 1830's do you see a sudden sharp drop in immigration?

    _____

    b. Why might this be? _____

    _____

4. a. When during the 1850's do you see a sharp drop in immigration?

    _____

    b. Why might this be? _____

    _____

5. Immigration from Ireland went from 51,752 in 1846 to 105,536 in 1847.

    a. How big an increase is this expressed as a percentage? _____

    b. What might be the reason for this increase? _____

    _____

6. a. Why did immigration drop in the early 1860's? _____

    _____

    b. Why was immigration back up to high levels in 1866? _____

    _____

Extra Challenge: Construct a graph showing immigrants as a percentage of the total U.S. population during the years from 1800 to 1865.

Focus on U.S. History:
The Era of Expansion and Reform

Coming to the United States

The trip across the Atlantic Ocean for poor people was not a pleasant cruise!
Read this description from the early 1800's.

Irish Emigrants Aboard the Ship *Polly*

Around me were the emigrants, some lying still, some sick, others talking, laughing, or quarreling. Women were cooking food, old men were smoking pipes, and the air was close and stifling. Cursing and groaning was heard on every side.

The packet *Polly*, of Waterford, must have been as bad as any slaver that ever skulked the "Middle Passage" with battened-down hatches. She was 202 tons burden and carried 450-odd steerage [the area below deck] passengers. They were so thick between decks that the air became putrid, and whenever her sick squads were ordered up the gangways, one or more was sure to die with the first gulp of fresh air. The steerage became pestilential [deadly] before our voyage was half over, for the emigrants' beds were never cleaned and whole families literally wallowed in poisonous filth. The bodies of men and women, and their tattered garments, were encrusted and impregnated with the most offensive matter. Typhus fever and dysentery soon broke out and then the mortality raged fearfully.

…When we made the first light, off Cape Ann, we had 186 left out of 450-odd passengers, and some of these died before landing.

Directions: What would make a person willing to undergo such a terrible and risky voyage?
Imagine you are one of the Irish emigrants described above. The year is 1848.

1. Who are you?

2. Why are you making this trip?

3. What are your hopes and expectations about life in the United States?

4. What actual conditions—economic and social—do you experience once you're here?

After you've written responses to these questions, you could use them to write a journal or story about your immigration experience.

Emigrants leaving Ireland

African Americans and the Growth of Slavery

The objectives of this unit are to help students understand how and why slavery grew rapidly after 1800, how African Americans coped with life as slaves, and how free African Americans found little equality in the North. Eli Whitney's invention of the cotton gin in 1793 revolutionized southern agri–culture. Cotton growing became very profitable throughout the lower South, creating a high demand for black slaves. Treated as property, enslaved African Americans nevertheless developed their own culture, with strong family and religious values. They resisted slavery in a variety of ways, from small acts of sabotage to escape attempts to armed violence. Blacks who lived free in the North weren't subject to the abuses of slavery, but they were denied the right to vote and denied equal opportunities in housing, education, and jobs. This unit's activities are designed to draw students into a better understanding of antebellum slavery.

Student Activities

Graphing Slavery presents students with popula-tion figures from states representative of the coun-try's various regions. From the figures, students create five pie charts showing the percentages of black and white populations in those states. The Extra Challenge asks students to relate the pie chart findings to the slavery debate issues examined in Unit 5.

Slave Voices presents former slaves' own words about their lives. Students use these passages, and other readings, to write an account of slave life, in the first or third person.

Forms of Resistance quotes some slaves on the ways they devised to resist their white masters. This serves as a prompt for students to put themselves in the place of a slave in the antebellum South and then list the simple, everyday ways they could resist their enslavement.

Slavery Time Line lists events significant in the history of slavery in the antebellum United States and asks students to create a time line with dates and descriptions of the events.

Secret Messages presents the lyrics of four slave songs and challenges students to interpret the messages hidden behind the face meanings of the words.

Free Blacks in the North gives Alexis de Tocqueville's description of conditions free blacks faced in northern cities in 1832. From this, students will identify ways in which life for free blacks was unequal in various specific aspects. The Extra Chal-lenge asks students to compare blacks' place in soci-ety in the antebellum North and South.

African Americans and the Growth of Slavery

The Revival of Slavery

It was a great breakthrough when Eli Whitney invented the cotton gin in 1793. Now cotton seeds could be separated from cotton fiber quickly and efficiently. Northern and British textile mills hungered for cotton. Now people could make a lot of money growing cotton in the South—white farm owners, that is.

Eli Whitney's cotton gin

The American Revolution had inspired people with ideas of freedom and equality. Some owners freed their slaves in response. Others let their slaves go because southern farms weren't earning much money anymore. The soil was worn out.

The cotton gin reversed this process. Now slaves were needed, and valuable. A big "internal trade" grew up: Slaves were sold from the upper South to the cotton lands of the lower South. Innumerable slave families were torn apart in the process. The South became firmly wedded to cotton farming and slavery.

The Conditions of Slavery

Enslaved African Americans on southern plantations made their own culture within the imposed culture of slavery. You can read about this in Book 2 of this series, *Focus on U.S. History: The Era of Colonization and Settlement.* The slaves blended aspects of African religious beliefs with Christianity. They formed extended families. Especially, they used music to ease their life and even feel joyous on occasion.

Life under slavery varied depending on the master and the overseer. Some masters treated their slaves fairly well—except that the slaves were denied their liberty. For most slaves, though, life was unending work with little leisure. Often they didn't get enough food or clothing. They lived with the constant threat of whippings and other physical abuse.

Slave Resistance

It's no surprise, then, that slaves resisted in many ways. They acted clumsy. They acted ignorant. They acted lazy. They broke things; they acted as though they couldn't understand instructions; they worked slowly.

Also, they escaped, or tried to. Many of their songs carried coded messages about escape. The meanings, not understood by whites, sang of the Underground Railroad, the rivers to the North, the stars to follow along the way.

Some slaves felt driven to violence.

But whites quickly stopped all of these uprisings.

Gabriel Prosser organized a rebellion plot in Virginia in 1800.	**Denmark Vesey** bought his freedom in South Carolina and then organized a revolt in 1822.	**Nat Turner** led an uprising that killed many white plantation dwellers in Virginia in 1831.

(continued)
Focus on U.S. History:
The Era of Expansion and Reform

Free Blacks

Free blacks were at best semifree. Many lived in northern cities, where leaders established African-American churches, schools, and community groups. Richard Allen, for example, founded the African Methodist Episcopal Zion Church in Philadelphia in 1816.

But free blacks still experienced many forms of unequal treatment:

- Most northern states took away free blacks' right to vote during the 1800's.
- Free blacks' opportunities for education, decent housing, and jobs were limited.

- Whites who resented competition from blacks for jobs rioted in northern cities in the 1830's, attacking blacks and their homes.

Some blacks, and whites too, promoted return to Africa for blacks. The American Colonization Society was supported by many leading whites. It bought land in Africa and set up the Republic of Liberia. But for most blacks, the United States was their native land. They wanted to stay and work to improve their status and help get rid of slavery.

Slaves desperate to escape could be quite ingenious. Henry "Box" Brown had a friend nail him inside a wooden box. He then shipped the box—via wagon, railroad, and steamboat—to Philadelphia. "Box" Brown spent part of the trip on his head, even though the box was marked "This side up with care." He reached free soil safely.

Graphing Slavery

Here are some black/white population figures from the 1850 U.S. census. Each state represents a different region of the United States.

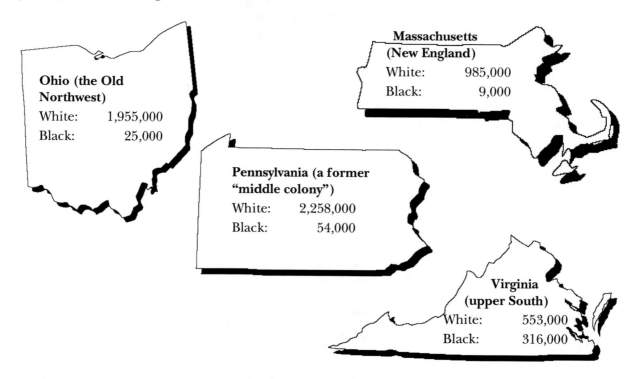

Ohio (the Old Northwest)
White: 1,955,000
Black: 25,000

Massachusetts (New England)
White: 985,000
Black: 9,000

Pennsylvania (a former "middle colony")
White: 2,258,000
Black: 54,000

Virginia (upper South)
White: 553,000
Black: 316,000

Directions: Create five pie charts showing the percentage of white and black population in each of these states. Then develop a question-answer series interpreting the pie charts. (For example, ask why the black/white percentages differ between the upper South and lower South.)

Extra Challenge: Explain how these population figures affected each region's stand on the slavery debate issue (see Unit 5).

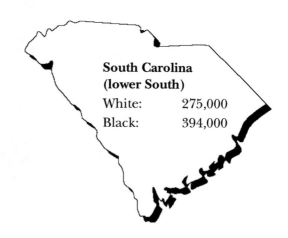

South Carolina (lower South)
White: 275,000
Black: 394,000

*Focus on U.S. History:
The Era of Expansion and Reform*

Slave Voices

Life as a slave varied, depending on the owner and the type of work required. Here are some slaves' own words about their lives.

Madison Bruin, former slave

Ole Marster was good to us. He give us plenty of good food. I git plenty of whippin's, but he never beat us hard....Ole Marster, he beat me and his son just the same.

Betty Powers, former slave

All the rations are measured out on Sunday morning.....'Twarn't enough for the heavy eaters....The short rations caused lots of trouble, 'cause the blacks have to steal food. 'Twas a whipping if they get caught. The colored folks are in a hell of a fix if they can't do the work 'cause they're weak [from hunger]. 'Twas a whipping then for sure.

Hilliard Yellerday, former slave

When a girl became a woman, she was required to go to a man and become a mother. There was generally a form of marriage. The master read a paper to them telling them they were man and wife. Some were married by the master laying down a broom and the two slaves, man and woman, would jump over it. The master would then tell them they were man and wife, and they could go to bed together.

Mary Gaffney, former slave

When a slave died, we just dug a hole in the ground, built a fence around it, and piled him in. No singing, no preaching or praying, ever took place during slavery time. Master would say, "Well, he was a pretty good Negro. Guess he will go to Heaven, all right." And that was about all there was to a Negro funeral, then. We would not even shed a tear, because he was gone where there would not be any more slaves. That was all the slave thought about, then: not being a slave. Because slavery time was hell.

Rachel Cruze, former slave

I was born on the farm of Major William Holden....My father was William Holden, Jr., the youngest child of Major Holden. My mother, Eliza Mobley, was the colored cook....I lived in Old Major's house as a member of the family all those years.

(continued)

Slave Voices *(continued)*

Jacob Manson, former slave

We worked all day an' some of the nights an' a slave who make a week, even after doin' that, was lucky if he got off without gettin' a beatin'. We had poor food, and the young slaves was fed out of troughs.

…The children were looked after by the old slave women who were unable to work in the fields, while the mothers of the babies worked. The women plowed and did other work as the men did. No books or learning of any kind was allowed.

Emily Dixon, former slave

On Sundays, we would git together in the woods an' have worship. We could go to the white folks' church, but we wanted to go where we could sing all the way through, an' hum along, an' shout—you all know; just turn loose like.

Mary Reynolds, former slave

Solomon the overseer beat [the slaves] with a big whip and Massa look on. The blacks better not stop in the fields when they hear them [the slaves being beaten] yellin'. They cut the flesh 'most to the bones, and some they was, when they taken them out of stock and put them on the beds, they never got up again.

Florence Napier, former slave

I sure enjoyed myself on the old plantation, and we-uns all had a good time. Always have plenty to eat. Master used to say, "The colored folks raised the food, an' they's entitled to all they wants." Same with the clothes.

Josiah Henson, former slave

Common as are slave-auctions in the southern states, and naturally as a slave may look forward to the time when he will be put up on the block, still the full misery of the event … is never understood till the actual experience comes. … My [five] brothers and sisters were bid off first, and one by one, while my mother, paralyzed by grief, held me by the hand. … Then I was offered to assembled purchasers. … I must have been then between five and six years old. I seem to see and hear my poor weeping mother now.

(continued)

Slave Voices *(continued)*

Directions: Use what you have read here, and other slave narratives, to write an account of slave life. This could be in the first person—you are a slave in the prewar South, or a visitor from the North or England, or a member of the slave-owning family, for example. Or your narrative could be a historical essay. In your account, be sure to include the following:

- the negative aspects of slave life, for slaves, owners, and overseers;
- the ways in which slaves held on to their humanity and self-worth;
- any possible positive aspects of slave life.

Whipping a slave

Forms of Resistance

Sometimes slaves revolted violently. Many tried to escape. Most common, though, was passive resistance—small acts that white slave owners and overseers might not catch on to. Here are some examples of passive resistance.

Rachel Cruze, Tennessee slave

Old Henry never ceased groaning and holding his side.... Dr. Sneed finally arrived and examined Henry thoroughly. Then he gravely ordered some medicine to be given regularly, with complete rest.... The doctor leaned over and whispered, "Julia, there is not a damn thing the matter with Henry."

Anonymous female slave

"Don't say I'm wicked [for stealing].... It's all right for us poor colored people to appropriate whatever of the white folks' blessings the Lord puts in our way."

Anonymous female slave

"Old Mistress got sick, and I would fan her with a brush, to keep the flies off her. I would hit her all in the face. Sometimes I would make out I was asleep and beat her in the face."

Directions: Suppose you are a slave in the antebellum (prewar) South. List the simple, everyday ways you could resist, or rebel, against your enslavement. Include the examples given above.

_____   _____

_____   _____

_____   _____

_____   _____

_____   _____

_____   _____

_____   _____

Slavery Time Line

Directions: With classmates, construct a time line of these important events in the history of slavery in the United States in the 1800's. (Hint: These events are listed in the order in which they occurred over time.) Include brief descriptions of each. Illustrations would add to your time line.

Fugitive Slave Law

invention of the cotton gin

first convention of abolition societies

Gabriel Prosser's revolt

importation of slaves into the U.S. forbidden

American Colonization Society founded

Missouri Compromise

Liberia founded

Denmark Vesey's revolt

Freedom's Journal starts publishing

Nat Turner's revolt

The Liberator starts publishing

various antislavery societies are founded

mob violence against blacks and abolition breaks out

Elijah Lovejoy is killed

the *Amistad* revolt

Douglass makes his first antislavery speech

the *Creole* revolt

Free Soil party is formed

Compromise of 1850

Uncle Tom's Cabin is published in book form

Kansas-Nebraska Act

Republican party is formed

Dred Scott decision

John Brown's raid

Nat Turner is captured.

Secret Messages

Slaves expressed their intents to escape slavery in their songs. Whites thought many of the words were about Bible stories—which they were, on one level. Read these lyrics:

Go Down, Moses

When Israel was in Egypt land;
    Let my people go;
Oppressed so hard they could not stand;
    Let my people go.

Chorus:
Go down, Moses,
    Way down in Egypt land,
Tell ole Pharaoh
    To let my people go.

No more shall they in bondage toil,
    Let my people go;
Let them come out with Egypt's spoil,
    Let my people go.
(*Chorus*)

O 'twas a dark and dismal night,
    Let my people go;
When Moses led the Israelites,
    Let my people go.
(*Chorus*)

The Lord told Moses what to do,
    Let my people go;
To lead the children of Israel through,
    Let my people go.
(*Chorus*)

Steal Away

Steal away, steal away,
    Steal away to Jesus;
Steal away, steal away home,
    I ain't got long to stay here.

My Lord calls me;
    He calls me by the thunder;
The trumpet sounds within-a my soul;
    I ain't got long to stay here.

Chorus: Steal away . . . .

O, Wasn't That a Wide River

O, wasn't that a wide river,
    That river of Jordan, Lord,
Wide river,
    There's one more river to cross.

O, the river of Jordan is so wide,
    One more river to cross;
I don't know how to get on the other side,
    One more river to cross.

Follow the Drinking Gourd

Follow the drinking gourd,
Follow the drinking gourd,
    For the old man is a-waiting
    For to carry you to freedom,
Follow the drinking gourd.

(continued)

Secret Messages *(continued)*

Directions: Ferret out the hidden meanings of the songs by answering these questions.

1. (a) What event in the Bible does "Go Down, Moses" tell about? _____

_____

   (b) What are black slaves saying about their intentions in this song? _____

_____

   (c) What black person are slaves singing about in "Moses"? How does this person relate to the words of the song? _____

_____

_____

2. When slaves sing about "stealing away," what two things are they referring to?

_____

_____

3. (a) What and where is the actual River Jordan? _____

_____

   (b) What are slaves actually referring to when they sing about crossing "the river of Jordan"?

_____

4. (a) What is the "drinking gourd"? _____

_____

   (b) Why do the slaves sing about following it? _____

_____

Extra Challenge: Sing/perform these songs in class.

Focus on U.S. History:
The Era of Expansion and Reform

Free Blacks in the North

Freedom was certainly preferable to slavery. But how free were blacks living in the North? A French traveler and author named Alexis de Tocqueville described conditions in 1832.

It is true that in the North of the Union marriages may be legally contracted between Negroes and whites; but public opinion would stigmatize as infamous a man who should connect himself with a Negress, and it would be difficult to cite a single instance of such a union. The electoral franchise has been conferred upon the Negroes in almost all the states in which slavery has been abolished, but if they come forward to vote, their lives are in danger. If oppressed, they may bring an action at law, but they will find none but whites among their judges; and although they may legally serve as jurors, prejudice repels them from that office. The same schools do not receive the children of the black and of the European. In the theaters gold cannot procure a seat for the servile race beside their former masters; in the hospitals they lie apart; and although they are allowed to invoke the same God as the whites, it must be at a different altar and in their own churches, with their own clergy. The gates of heaven are not closed against them, but their inferiority is continued to the very confines of the other world. When the Negro dies, his bones are cast aside, and the distinction of condition prevails even in the equality of death. Thus the Negro is free, but he can share neither the rights, nor the pleasures, nor the labor, nor the afflictions, nor the tomb of him whose equal he has been declared to be; and he cannot meet him upon fair terms in life or in death.

Directions: Describe here the ways in which northern blacks led a less than equal life in the 1830's, according to de Tocqueville.

1. death: _____   5. medical care: _____

_____   _____

2. education: _____   6. religion: _____

_____   _____

3. entertainment: _____   7. voting: _____

_____   _____

4. legal system: _____

Extra Challenge: Write an essay comparing blacks' place in society in the North and the South in the mid-1800's (the antebellum period), or present the comparison in chart form.

Focus on U.S. History:
The Era of Expansion and Reform

Politics

The objectives of this unit are to help students understand how American political life changed in the Jacksonian era and how the debate over slavery increasingly dominated U.S. politics. The election of Andrew Jackson as president in 1828 ushered in the era of the "common man" in American political life. Led by the West, states moved to universal white male suffrage. People from all walks of life participated in national and state politics—campaigning, voting, and serving in office. Underlying all this was the simmering slavery question, regularly rising to a boil as new states and territories joined the nation. Should they be free or slave? The country's leaders managed to avoid disunion through the Missouri Compromise of 1820, the nullification crisis of the 1830's, and the great Compromise of 1850. But the issue—Thomas Jefferson's "fire bell in the night"—continued to threaten the Union. This unit's activities are designed to draw students into an understanding of the political issues of this era.

Student Activities

Political Cartoons presents the "King Andrew" cartoon and asks students to interpret its symbols and meanings. The Extra Challenge broadens students' appreciation of political cartooning by asking them to draw a political cartoon of their own.

Political Parties and the Issues provides a frame for students to identify the differences between the Democratic and Whig parties on major issues of the day. The Extra Challenge asks students to identify one main issue for several minor parties.

A Gallery of Presidents checks students' knowledge of the antebellum U.S. presidents. Given pictures and thumbnail sketches of 13 presidents, students name the men and then add their dates in office.

The Slavery Issue uses the Mapping Territorial Expansion maps from Unit 1 to show the division between slave and free states and relates the Unit 4 pie charts to the maps. The second part of this activity provides frames in which students briefly describe the main slavery-related issues, laws, and/or compromises.

Reaching a Compromise presents the divisive slavery issues that were the subject of the Compromise of 1850 and the North/West versus South positions on each. Students are challenged to work as northerners, westerners, and southerners of the era to find a solution to each issue.

Slavery West of the Mississippi—Yes or No? presents original source quotes from debates in the U.S. Congress on this question. Students summarize the arguments pro and con and then role-play a congressional debate on the question.

Regions and Issues presents a framework for students to identify the issues that divided the three regions of the nation in the antebellum period— North, South, and West.

Politics

The "Age of the Common Man" and the Debate over Slavery

Jackson's Democracy

Political life in the United States changed during the 1820's. Andrew Jackson's election as U.S. president was a symbol and a result of those changes. Jackson was a war hero and an Indian fighter, a man of the frontier. (He was also a wealthy plantation and slave owner, but the voters didn't see him that way.)

Andrew Jackson

Jackson's election as president in 1828 was hailed (by some people) as a triumph of the "common man." Politics was now more democratic. The "common man" both voted and served in office. Regular people became their own leaders.

Western states led the way by opening the vote to all white males, not just those who owned property. More and more officials were voted into office, not appointed. After a while, the eastern states followed suit. Political campaigns became more boisterous as political parties used slogans, gimmicks, and hoopla to attract voters. Oddly, at the same time, racial prejudice prompted most states to take the vote *away* from free African-Americans.

Jackson's reception at the White House after his inaugural turned into a mob scene. His followers enthusiastically invaded the mansion and created chaos. They ruined fine carpets with their muddy boots, broke delicate chairs, and ripped satin upholstery. Jackson's opponents immediately tagged him "King Mob."

Political Parties

Jackson was the head of the Democratic party. His followers came from all sections of the country and all walks of life. But Democrats shared some basic ideas. They were champions of the ordinary (white) man (not woman). They promoted this man's ability to serve in public office and his right to have a chance at an education and economic opportunity. Democrats didn't trust big banks, big business, or upper-class privileges.

During what year in U.S. history did this country have three presidents?

Jackson's opponents formed the Whig party. Whigs tended to favor a strong national government, including a national bank. They distrusted rule by the "common man." At the same time, they thought Jackson himself wielded too much power and called him "King Andrew." The Whigs did manage to elect a president—William Henry Harrison, in 1840. But they ran a campaign that avoided the issues.

The Slavery Issue

Politics was getting more open and equal. But more and more, politics in the 1800's was also focusing on the slavery issue. Under the Constitution, each state controlled slavery within its boundaries. But the Constitution gave Congress control over slavery in the territories. And as you learned in Unit 1, the United States acquired a lot of territory in the first half of the 1800's. Should Congress allow slavery in these territories or not? The question was impossible to avoid.

(continued)

Focus on U.S. History:
The Era of Expansion and Reform

The Missouri Compromise. The first serious crisis on the slavery issue in this period came up when Missouri was ready to become a state. Missouri had many slave owners and slaves, so it would definitely be a slave state. Northerners objected; this would upset the balance in Congress between slave and free states. The men in Congress worked out a compromise in 1820: Missouri would enter the Union as a slave state; Maine would enter at the same time as a free state. Slavery was also barred from the rest of the Louisiana Purchase territory. (It wasn't practical to have it there anyway, so Southerners didn't object.)

The Nullification Crisis. Northern manufacturers favored high **tariffs**—duties paid on goods brought into the United States from overseas. This protected the goods the northerners made. Southerners favored low tariffs because they didn't have much industry and had to buy their manufactured goods. Tariffs raised the price of these goods.

Congress lowered tariffs in 1832, but not enough to suit southerners. John C. Calhoun of South Carolina urged his state to **nullify** the tariff law. South Carolina did this—it declared the tariff law void, saying it had no legal effect in their state. President Jackson said he'd send troops to South Carolina to enforce the law. The South Carolina radicals backed down. Men from the North and the West in Congress agreed to compromise, with a somewhat lower tariff.

What did all this have to do with slavery? The South Carolina radicals felt that as soon as they gave in on the tariff, northerners would press for the end of slavery. What if northerners pushed a law through Congress outlawing slavery? If the radicals couldn't nullify a law like that, maybe they would have to **secede**—withdraw—from the Union to keep slavery going. They began working to get other southern states to come over to their side.

The Wilmot Proviso. In 1846, during the Mexican War, Congressman David Wilmot proposed a law barring slavery from any territory the United States might acquire from Mexico. Senator Calhoun answered with resolutions saying that Congress couldn't bar slavery from any territory. Senator Lewis Cass offered up the idea of "**popular sovereignty**"—allowing the people in each territory to decide for or against slavery there themselves. The issue remained up in the air.

The Compromise of 1850

After winning the Mexican War, the United States gained another huge chunk of land: California and the New Mexico territory. Now the questions brought up by the Wilmot proviso had to be solved. Southerners wanted slavery in the territories; northerners did not.

Some southerners talked about seceding, taking their states out of the United States, over this issue.

Two great politicians and orators, old and at the end of their careers, saved the day. Henry Clay, a senator from Kentucky, proposed this compromise:

(continued)

Focus on U.S. History:
The Era of Expansion and Reform

California: Enter Union now as a free state.	**New Mexico and Utah Territories:** Organize without mention of slavery; settlers to decide this later.	**District of Columbia (Washington, D.C.):** End slave trade—but not slavery—here.
Fugitive (runaway) slaves: Pass and enforce a strict law saying runaway slaves in the North must be captured and returned to their masters in the South.		

(The fifth part of the compromise was that the federal government would assume the Texas national debt. In return, disputed land along the Texas border would become part of the New Mexico Territory.)

Daniel Webster, a senator from Massachusetts, agreed. Senator Calhoun of South Carolina, another great speaker, disagreed. (Calhoun, at this time, could not speak due to medical problems. Senator Mason of Virginia spoke for him.) The debate in the Senate was magnificent. In the end, South, West, and North accepted the Compromise. The Union was saved—for now.

Runaway slave

Name _____

Date _____

Political Cartoons

Like those of today, cartoonists of the 1800's made sharp points about people and politics in their drawings. Here's an example: a political cartoon about President Andrew Jackson.

King Andrew the First, Born to Rule

(continued)

Focus on U.S. History:
The Era of Expansion and Reform

Political Cartoons *(continued)*

Directions: Answer the following questions about this cartoon.

1. Why did Jackson's opponents call him "King Andrew"?

2. What symbols does the cartoonist use to make his point?

3. What would Jackson's supporters say is unfair about this cartoon?

Extra Challenge: Draw a political cartoon of your own. Use a current event as your subject—national, local, or school. Use the space below to sketch your ideas or jot down notes.

Political Parties and the Issues

Directions: How did the two major political parties of the 1820's to 1850's stand on issues of the day? You'll know at a glance after you fill in this chart.

Democratic Party	Issue	Whig Party
	slavery	
	central government versus state powers	
	the economy	
	immigrants	
	democracy; participation by common people in government	
	the spoils system	

Extra Challenge: Identify the main issue for each of these parties:

1. National Republican _____

2. Free Soil _____

3. American (Know-Nothing) _____

4. Liberty _____

Focus on U.S. History:
The Era of Expansion and Reform

A Gallery of Presidents

Directions: Some of the antebellum U.S. presidents aren't too memorable. Others are. Check your knowledge of them by naming each man shown. Also, add the years he was president.

1.

This Virginia author of the Bill of Rights was president when British soldiers set fire to the White House during the War of 1812.

Name: _____

Dates in office: _____

2.

The election of this popular, well-known general from Tennessee ushered in the era of the "common man" in U.S. politics.

Name: _____

Dates in office: _____

3.

"Old Rough and Ready" was a soldier, not a politician. He died after being president for only 16 months.

Name: _____

Dates in office: _____

4.

This aristocrat ran for president as a log-cabin-type person. "Old Tippecanoe" caught a cold at his inaugural and died 31 days later.

Name: _____

Dates in office: _____

(continued)

© 1997 J. Weston Walch, Publisher

72

A Gallery of Presidents *(continued)*

5.

This author of the Declaration of Independence was the third U.S. president, and the second one from Virginia.

Name: _____

Dates in office: _____

6.

This hardworking president from Tennessee led the U.S. in a war with Mexico.

Name: _____

Dates in office: _____

7.

This Virginia aristocrat presided over the "Era of Good Feelings" and told Europe to stay out of the Americas.

Name: _____

Dates in office: _____

8.

This man from New Hampshire was a "dark horse" candidate chosen when the Democrats couldn't agree on anyone well known.

Name: _____

Dates in office: _____

(continued)

Focus on U.S. History:
The Era of Expansion and Reform

A Gallery of Presidents *(continued)*

9.

This New Yorker was a good friend and the vice president of Jackson, but he lost his bid for reelection in the "log cabin campaign."

Name: _____

Dates in office: _____

10.

This bachelor from Pennsylvania became president even though he got fewer popular votes than his opponent. He didn't do much as president.

Name: _____

Dates in office: _____

11.

This gentleman from Virginia was the first U.S. vice president to become chief executive when the elected president died.

Name: _____

Dates in office: _____

12.

Like his father, this serious son of a president couldn't get himself elected to a second term.

Name: _____

Dates in office: _____

13.

This New Yorker was never elected president. He got trade started with Japan.

Name: _____

Dates in office: _____

Focus on U.S. History:
The Era of Expansion and Reform

The Slavery Issue

Part 1 Directions: Slavery was a constant issue in U.S. politics during the first half of the 1800's. Go back to your Mapping Territorial Expansion maps, which show the United States in 1821 and in 1853.

- On both maps, color the slave states and territories one color. Use a different color for the free states and territories.
- Is the balance about the same for both maps?
- Do the pie charts you created in Unit 4 accurately predict whether states are slave or free in 1853?

Part 2 Directions: In the boxes below are slavery-related issues, laws, and/or compromises. Briefly explain what each one is about, as it relates to slavery.

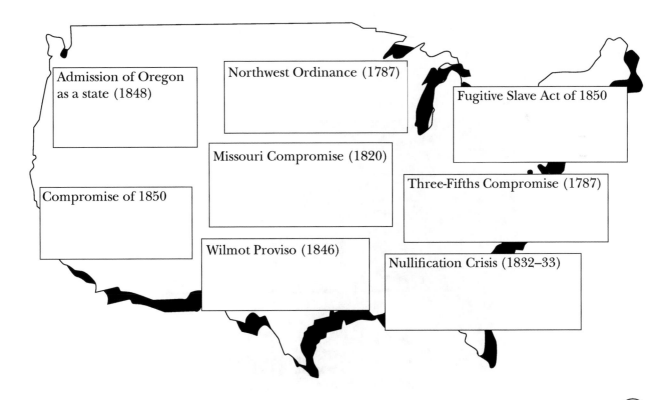

Admission of Oregon as a state (1848)

Northwest Ordinance (1787)

Fugitive Slave Act of 1850

Missouri Compromise (1820)

Compromise of 1850

Three-Fifths Compromise (1787)

Wilmot Proviso (1846)

Nullification Crisis (1832–33)

Reaching a Compromise

Henry Clay, John Calhoun, Daniel Webster, and other members of Congress worked hard to settle issues that divided the North and South. They had to compromise—find middle-ground solutions they could all agree to.

Directions: How would you have settled the tough issues these men grappled with? With classmates, work out a set of solutions to these thorny problems. (Your teacher will divide you into groups of northerners, southerners, and westerners.)

Issue: Slavery and the Slave Trade in Washington, D.C.

North/West position: Against both.

Southern position: For both.

Issue: Admission of California to the Union

North/West position: Free—admit now.

Southern position: Don't admit as free, or wait until a new slave state also joins the Union.

Issue: Slavery in the U.S. Territories of Utah and New Mexico

North/West position: Forbid it.

Southern position: Allow it.

Issue: Fugitive Slave Laws

North/West position: Don't enforce these laws.

Southern position: Enforce these laws strictly.

The Verdict of the People, by artist George Caleb Bingham

*Focus on U.S. History:
The Era of Expansion and Reform*

Slavery West of the Mississippi—Yes or No?

The United States acquired a lot of territory west of the Mississippi River. New states would be carved out of these territories. Should slavery be allowed in the new states and territories? That was a hotly debated question in the 1800's. Below are some views expressed in debates in the U.S. Congress.

Directions: After you read these views, summarize, in list form, the arguments for and against allowing or outlawing slavery in new states and territories. Then role-play a debate in Congress on the question.

John Taylor, congressman from New York (1819)

Here I might [remind] my opponents of their own declarations on the subject of slavery. How often and how eloquently have they deplored its existence among them? Gentlemen have now an opportunity of putting their principles into practice; if they have tried slavery and found it a curse; if they desire to dissipate the gloom with which it covers their land, I call upon them to exclude it from the territory in question; plant not its seeds in this uncorrupt soil.

…If the rejection of slavery will tend to discourage emigration from the South, will not its admission have the same effect in relation to the North and East? …Do you believe these people will settle in a country where they must take rank with slaves? Having neither the ability nor will to hold slaves themselves, they labor cheerfully while labor is honorable; make it disgraceful, they will despise it.

Philip Barbour, congressman from Virginia (1819)

[Missouri] would obviously labor under [a] disadvantage in relation to the other states; that, whereas the older free states might introduce slavery, Missouri could not.…A prohibition of the importation of slaves would, in almost every instance, be tantamount to a prohibition of the emigration of the southern people to the state of Missouri.

William Darlington, congressman from Pennsylvania (1820)

Rather would I call slavery a contagious disease in the body politic. Like smallpox, it ought to be confined in the smallest possible limits.

Benjamin Hardin, congressman from Kentucky (1820)

We have already surrendered to the non-slaveholding states all that region of the American empire between the great rivers Ohio and Mississippi; and if you tear from us that immense country west of the Mississippi, we may at once surrender at discretion, crouch at the feet of our adversaries, and beg mercy of our proud and haughty victors.

(continued)

© 1997 J. Weston Walch, Publisher

Focus on U.S. History:
The Era of Expansion and Reform

Slavery West of the Mississippi—Yes or No? *(continued)*

Robert W. Reid, congressman from Georgia (1820)

Slaves, divided among many masters [throughout the territories], will enjoy greater privileges and comforts than those who, cooped within a narrow sphere and under few owners, will be doomed to drag a long, heavy, and clanking chain through the space of their existence. Danger from insurrection will diminish.... In proportion as few slaves are possessed by the same individual will he look with less reluctance to the prospect of their ultimate liberation. Emancipations will become common.

Daniel Webster, senator from Massachusetts (1848)

In the [Constitutional] Convention, and in the first Congress, it was conceded that slavery was a state institution, and that Congress had no power over it.... The Southern senators say we deprive them of the right to go into these newly acquired territories with their property. We certainly do not prevent them from going into these territories with what is in general law called property. But these states have by their local laws created a property in persons, and they cannot carry those local laws with them. Slavery is created and exists by a local law, which is limited to a certain section.

Thomas Corwin, senator from Ohio (1848)

The men of 1776 did not believe that one man was born "booted and spurred" to ride another. And, if, as they said, no man was born to *rule* another, did it not follow that no man could rightfully be born to *serve* another? . . . They declared slavery an evil, a wrong, a prejudice to free colonies, a social mischief, and a political evil; and, if these were denied, they replied, "These truths are self-evident."

John C. Calhoun, senator from South Carolina (1847)

Sir, the day that the balance between the two sections of the country—the slaveholding states and the non-slaveholding states—is destroyed, is a day that will not be far removed from political revolution, anarchy, civil war, and widespread disaster....

How, then, do we stand in reference to this territorial question—this public domain of ours? ... Sir, these territories are the property of the states united; held jointly for their common use. And is it consistent with justice, is it consistent with equality, that any portion of the partners, outnumbering another portion, shall oust them of this common property of theirs—shall pass any law which shall proscribe the citizens of other portions of the Union from emigrating with their property to the territories of the United States?

Regions and Issues

Where you lived in the United States affected how you looked at various issues. Fill in on this chart what your thoughts as an average white citizen were likely to be on the national issues named.

Issue	North	South	West
protective tariff			
sale of western lands			
internal improvements (roads, canals, railroads)			
national bank			
slavery			
nullification			

79

Focus on U.S. History:
The Era of Expansion and Reform

Reform Movements and the National Culture

The objectives of this unit are to help students to understand better the reform movements of the antebellum period and the development of a distinctive American national culture. Reformers in this era worked to right many of society's problems, inspired in part by the religious revival of the Second Great Awakening. While reformers found many ills to cure, the most intense reform movement was abolitionism. All abolitionists wanted to end slavery in the United States, but they advocated several different positions, from gradualism to immediate emancipation; some advocated violence while others urged colonization. The abolition movement gave birth to a second great reform movement that continues to this day: women's rights. Women abolitionists, sensitized to the concept of equal rights, noted that they were treated unequally within the abolition movement as well as in society as a whole. They banded together to correct these injustices. This unit's activities are designed to draw students into a better understanding of these aspects of antebellum society.

Student Activities

Abolition Plans presents original source quotes expressing the range of opinions within the abolition movement. Questions guide students into identifying the different positions and the reasons for them. The Extra Challenge has students role-play a debate among antislavery activists holding different positions.

The Proslavery Response presents original source quotes expressing several justifications for continuing U.S. slavery. From this, and other readings, students develop responses to each proslavery point. They then role-play a debate between pro- and anti-slavery antebellum speakers.

The Rights of Women presents the Seneca Falls Declaration of Sentiments and guides students into a comparison between it and the Declaration of Independence, which it was modeled after.

Women's Grievances presents the list of women's grievances against men outlined in the Seneca Falls Declaration. Students identify the specific aspects of antebellum life the list protests about. The Extra Challenge asks students to identify the extent to which women were successful in getting action taken on these grievances.

An Age of Reform uses a matching game challenge to help students identify individual reformers with the reform issue they worked on. The Challenge Question helps students make the connection between the abolition movement and the movement for women's rights.

American Writers uses pictures and hints to help students identify outstanding antebellum American authors and their works. A suggested additional activity extends the national culture theme by asking students to create a class display of antebellum artwork.

Reform Movements and the National Culture

Ending Slavery

America in the 1800's was a nation bustling with industry, new types of transportation—and reform. Reformers worked for education for deaf people and blind people, for better treatment of mentally ill people, for public education and education for young women, and against alcohol. The most important reform movement of this era was **abolitionism**—the drive to abolish, or end, slavery in the United States.

While all abolitionists wanted to wipe out slavery, not all agreed on how to do this. William Lloyd Garrison firmly called for immediate abolition. He published his ideas in his newspaper, *The Liberator.* Sometimes when he gave speeches, mobs attacked him.

Frederick Douglass, a former slave, lectured often and eloquently for abolition. He also called for social, political, and economic equality for freed blacks. Many whites were uncomfortable with that idea. Some of them promoted groups to resettle free blacks in Africa (see Unit 4).

Other abolitionists were "gradualists." Pushing for an immediate end to slavery could break up the Union; the South would resist, violently. These reformers urged a gradual end to slavery, by passing laws and persuading southerners to free the slaves by their own choice.

Women's Rights

Abolitionism had an unexpected spin-off: It created a new reform movement. Women who were active in abolition circles found they were treated as second-class members. They weren't supposed to speak at public meetings. They weren't supposed to be active in politics.

Also, abolitionists argued that the Declaration of Independence said all men are created equal. If this applied to slaves, shouldn't it also apply to women? Like black slaves, nineteenth-century white women led very restricted lives. They were shut out of good jobs and college educations. By law, they were inferior to their husbands. They were supposed to stay home and be dutiful wives and attentive mothers.

Reformers Elizabeth Cady Stanton and Lucretia Mott organized the first national women's rights convention. Women gathered from all over at Seneca Falls, New York, in 1848. They issued a Declaration of Sentiments that used the Declaration of Independence as a model. It began, "We hold these truths to be self-evident: that all men and women are created equal." The women's rights movement had begun.

Elizabeth Cady Stanton

Lucretia Mott

(continued)

Focus on U.S. History:
The Era of Expansion and Reform

The Second Great Awakening

A great religious revival swept across the United States in the early 1800's. The same thing had happened in the 1700's; it was called the Great Awakening. This new revival was called, logically enough, the Second Great Awakening. Famous preachers like Charles Finney and Peter Cartwright traveled from town to town drawing thousands of people to great camp meetings. Their message: People must take their lives into their own hands and save themselves, because Judgment Day is coming soon.

The revivalists called for women to guide their families into leading better lives. This led many women into the next step, working to make all of society better. So the Second Great Awakening fed the reform movements of the 1800's.

The National Culture

During the first half of the 1800's, American writers began writing about American subjects. They created an American literature that was distinctly different from European writing. Here are some examples:

 **James Fenimore Cooper** wrote about Indians and settlers—frontier life.	 **Washington Irving** wrote about Dutch legends in New York's Hudson Valley.	 **Herman Melville** wrote about a New England whaling voyage.
 **Edgar Allan Poe** pioneered in writing detective stories and horror tales.	 **New Englanders** like **Ralph Waldo Emerson** invented a new system of thought called **transcendentalism**.	

American painters, too, created artwork that celebrated American people, events, and landscapes. The Hudson River School artists created sweeping, romantic landscapes of their region. John James Audubon recorded with great beauty and accuracy many of the birds of America. George Catlin lived among Native Americans on the Great Plains and recorded them and their way of life. Many more nineteenth-century artists and writers showed that a rough, boisterous republic could also produce great art and literature.

Abolition Plans

People who wished to see the slaves freed didn't all agree on how to accomplish this. Here are some of their views.

Thomas Jefferson, statesman (1781)

[Freed slaves] should be colonized to such place as the circumstances of the time should render most proper, sending them out with arms, implements of household and of the handicraft arts, seeds, pairs of the useful domestic animals, etc. to declare them a free and independent people, and extend to them our alliance and protection, till they shall have acquired strength....It will probably be asked, Why not retain and incorporate the blacks into the state? Deep-rooted prejudices entertained by the whites; ten thousand recollections, by the blacks, of the injuries they have sustained; new provocations; the real distinctions which nature has made; and many other circumstances, will divide us into parties, and produce convulsions which will probably never end but in the extermination of the one or the other race.

Jefferson

F. A. Tallmadge, New York abolitionist (1833)

Ought there not ... to be a feeling of conciliation between the people of this part of the United States and their southern neighbors, when it was a question which might lead to a civil war? Even if [abolitionists] had the power of giving freedom to two millions of slaves, could they think of doing so without compensating their owners? And where would those fine philanthropists get money enough for such an object? It would amount to more than the entire taxation of the United States. The only course by which the object could be attained was a gradual abolition. Let that be done, but at the same time let us conciliate our southern neighbors.

William Lloyd Garrison, Massachusetts abolitionist (1831)

Assenting to the "self-evident truth" maintained in the American Declaration of Independence, "that all men are created equal and endowed by their Creator with certain inalienable rights—among which are life, liberty and the pursuit of happiness," I shall strenuously contend for the immediate enfranchisement [freeing] of our slave population....On this subject, I do not wish to think, or speak, or write, with moderation. No! No! Tell a man whose house is on fire, to give a moderate alarm; tell him to moderately rescue his wife from the hands of the ravisher; tell the mother to gradually extricate her babe from the fire into which it has fallen;—but urge me not to use moderation in a cause like the present.

(continued)

Abolition Plans *(continued)*

William E. Channing, Unitarian minister (1837)

Channing

I have expressed my fears, that by the annexation of Texas, slavery is to be continued and extended. But I wish not to be understood as having the slightest doubt as to the approaching fall of the institution.... Fall it will and must.... The slaveholder must not imagine that he has nothing to do but fight with a few [antislavery] societies. These, of themselves, are nothing.... His battle is with the laws of human nature and irresistible tendencies of human affairs.... The world is against him, and the world's Maker.... Can he hope to sustain slavery against the moral feeling, the solemn sentence of the human race?

David Walker, black abolitionist (1829)

Remember, Americans, that we must and shall be free and enlightened as you are. Will you wait until we shall, under God, obtain our liberty by the crushing arm of power? Will it not be dreadful for you? I speak, Americans, for your good. We must and shall be free, I say, in spite of you. You may do your best to keep us in wretchedness and misery, to enrich you and your children, but God will deliver us from under you. And woe, woe, will be to you if we have to obtain our freedom by fighting. Throw away your fears and prejudices, then, and enlighten us and treat us like men, and we will like you more than we do now hate you. And tell us no more about colonization, for America is as much our country as it is yours.

Directions: Use what you've read to answer the following questions.

1. Why did some abolitionists favor sending freed slaves to Africa? Was this plan put into effect?

2. How did the positions of abolitionists like Garrison and Tallmadge differ?

3. How did abolitionists like Channing justify taking no immediate action against slavery?

4. What was the most radical approach to abolition? Was this approach put into action?

Extra Challenge: Role-play a debate among activists holding various positions on the abolition of slavery.

The Proslavery Response

How did people justify slavery? Here are some of their words.

Mr. Monroe, a Virginia slaveowner (1829)

Emancipate [the slaves], and what would be their condition? Four hundred thousand, or a greater number, of poor, without one cent of property—what would become of them? Disorganization would follow, and perfect confusion. They are separated from the rest of society, by a different color.…They must remain as poor, free from the control of their masters, and must soon fall upon the rest of the society, and resort to plunder for subsistence.

Mr. Moore, a Virginia slaveowner (1829)

…Although our slaves are by nature entitled to equal rights with the rest of the human race, and although it would be both our interest and our duty to send them out from amongst us, if any practicable scheme could be suggested …that yet, all questions as to their rights are questions between them and ourselves exclusively.…We are answerable for our injustice towards them, only to our own consciences, and to the Great God of all.…No foreign people or power has a right in any manner, under any circumstances … to interfere between them and us.

Thomas Roderic Dew, Virginia professor (1832)

With regard to the assertion that slavery is against the spirit of Christianity, we are ready to admit the general assertion, but deny most positively that there is any thing in the Old or New Testament which would go to show that slavery, when once introduced, ought at all events to be [abolished], or that the master commits any offense in holding slaves.

…Look to the slave-holding population of our country, and you everywhere find them characterized by noble and elevated sentiment, by humane and virtuous feelings.…We have no hesitation in affirming, that throughout the whole slave-holding country, the slaves of a good master are his warmest, most constant, and most devoted friends.…A merrier being does not exist on the face of the globe than the Negro slave of the United States.

…The scheme of deportation is utterly impracticable, and emancipation, with permission to remain, will produce [violence against whites].

Directions: Find other proslavery arguments. Then develop responses to each proslavery point the writer or speaker makes. (You may find some on the Abolition Plans pages.) Finish by role-playing a debate between pro- and anti-slavery speakers of the pre-Civil War era.

The Rights of Women

The Seneca Falls Convention of 1848 was the first women's rights meeting. Its Declaration of Sentiments used the Declaration of Independence as a model. Below are its opening paragraphs.

Seneca Falls Declaration of Sentiments

When, in the course of human events, it becomes necessary for one portion of the family of man to assume among the people of the earth a position different from that which they have hitherto occupied, but one in which the laws of nature and of nature's God entitle them, a decent respect to the opinions of mankind requires that they should declare the causes that impel them to such a course.

We hold these truths to be self-evident: that all men and women are created equal; that they are endowed by their Creator with certain inalienable rights; that among these are life, liberty, and the pursuit of happiness; that to secure these rights governments are instituted, deriving their just powers from the consent of the governed. Whenever any form of government becomes destructive of these ends, it is the right of those who suffer from it to refuse allegiance to it, and to insist upon the institution of a new government, laying its foundation on such principles, and organizing its powers in such form, as to them shall seem most likely to effect their safety and happiness.

Prudence, indeed, will dictate that governments long established should not be changed for light and transient causes.... But when a long train of abuses and usurpations, pursuing invariably the same object, evinces a design to reduce them under absolute despotism, it is their duty to throw off such government, and to provide new guards for their future security. Such has been the patient sufferance of the women under this government, and such is now the necessity which constrains them to demand the equal station to which they are entitled.

Directions:

1. Underline the parts of the Declaration of Sentiments that are different from the Declaration of Independence.

2. What are the main differences between this Declaration and the Declaration of Independence?

3. Do you think this expression of why the women are making their declaration is as effective and persuasive as the Declaration of Independence?

Elizabeth Cady Stanton

Focus on U.S. History:
The Era of Expansion and Reform

Women's Grievances

The Seneca Falls Declaration of Sentiments, like the Declaration of Independence, lists specific grievances—complaints—American women have against American men. Here is part of the list.

Seneca Falls List of Grievances

The history of mankind is a history of repeated injuries and usurpations on the part of man toward woman, having in direct object the establishment of an absolute tyranny over her. To prove this, let facts be submitted to a candid world.

- He has never permitted her to exercise her inalienable right to the elective franchise.

- He has compelled her to submit to laws, in the formation of which she had no voice.

- He has withheld from her rights which are given to the most ignorant and degraded men—both natives and foreigners.

- He has made her, if married, in the eye of the law, civilly dead.

- He has taken from her all right in property, even to the wages she earns.

- In the covenant of marriage, she is compelled to promise obedience to her husband, he becoming, to all intents and purposes, her master—the law giving him power to deprive her of her liberty, and to administer chastisement.

- He has so framed the laws of divorce, as to what shall be the proper causes, and …to whom the guardianship of the children shall be given, as to be wholly regardless of the happiness of women—the law, in all cases, going upon a false supposition of the supremacy of man, and giving all power into his hands.

- After depriving her of all rights as a married woman, if single, and the owner of property, he has taxed her to support a government which recognizes her only when her property can be made profitable to it.

- He has monopolized nearly all the profitable employments, and from those she is permitted to follow, she receives but a scanty remuneration [wages]….As a teacher of theology, medicine, or law, she is not known.

- He has denied her the facilities for obtaining a thorough education, all colleges being closed against her.

- He …[claims] apostolic authority for her exclusion from the ministry, and …from any public participation in the affairs of the church.

- He has created a false public sentiment by giving to the world a different code of morals for men and women, by which moral delinquencies which exclude women from society, are not only tolerated, but deemed of little account in man.

- He has usurped the prerogative of Jehovah himself, claiming it as his right to assign for her a sphere of action, when that belongs to her conscience and to her God.

(continued)

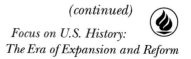

Focus on U.S. History:
The Era of Expansion and Reform

Women's Grievances *(continued)*

- He has endeavored, in every way that he could, to destroy her confidence in her own powers, to lessen her self-respect and to make her willing to lead a dependent and abject life.

Now, in view of the entire disfranchisement of one-half the people of this country, their social and religious degradation—in view of the unjust laws above mentioned, and because women do feel themselves aggrieved, oppressed, and fraudulently deprived of their most sacred rights, we insist that they have immediate admission to all the rights and privileges which belong to them as citizens of the United States.

Lucretia Mott

Directions: Explain here what specific situations the Declaration of Sentiments protests about.

Political Wrongs:

_____
_____
_____
_____
_____
_____
_____
_____

Social Wrongs:

_____
_____
_____
_____
_____
_____
_____
_____

Legal Wrongs:

_____
_____
_____
_____
_____
_____
_____
_____

Economic Wrongs:

_____
_____
_____
_____
_____
_____
_____
_____

Extra Challenge: How successful were women in the 1800's at having their grievances addressed? in the 1900's? Give specific details.

An Age of Reform

Directions: Reform movements flourished in the United States in the first half of the 1800's. Match each name on the right with the reform issue that person is identified with. (Write the letter of the reform issue next to the person's name. Some reform issues are associated with several names. Some names are associated with more than one reform issue.)

(a) education of blind people

(b) women's rights

(c) religious revivalism

(d) women's clothing

(e) education of deaf people

(f) prohibition (banning) of alcohol

(g) utopian communities

(h) free public education

(i) care of the mentally ill

(j) abolition of slavery

(k) college education for women

Dorothea Dix _____

Thomas Gallaudet _____

Elizabeth Cady Stanton _____

Charles Grandison Finney _____

Neal Dow _____

William Lloyd Garrison _____

Lyman Beecher _____

Sarah and Angela Grimké _____

Horace Mann _____

Dr. Samuel Gridley Howe _____

Robert Owen _____

Susan B. Anthony _____

Amelia Bloomer _____

Frederick Douglass _____

Mary Lyon _____

Lucretia Mott _____

Challenge Question: What connection do you see between the movements for abolition of slavery and for women's rights?

Focus on U.S. History:
The Era of Expansion and Reform

American Writers

Directions: American writing came into its own in the first part of the 1800's. Identify the writers and books below. The hints should help you!

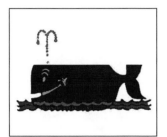

Hint: A whale of a tale.

Title: _____

Author: _____

Hint: Life in the woods.

Title: _____

Author: _____

Hint: The last of the tribe.

Title: _____

Author: _____

Hint: Yesterday's Stephen King.

Title (of one of his stories):

_____

Author: _____

Hint: Red alphabet.

Title: _____

Author: _____

Hint: Green poetry.

Title: _____

Author: _____

Hint: Native American "tune."

Title: _____

Author: _____

Hint: A really long nap.

Title: _____

Author: _____

Focus on U.S. History:
The Era of Expansion and Reform

ANSWER KEY
ADDITIONAL ACTIVITIES
ASSESSMENTS

Unit 1: Territorial Expansion

Mapping the Louisiana Purchase (page 6)

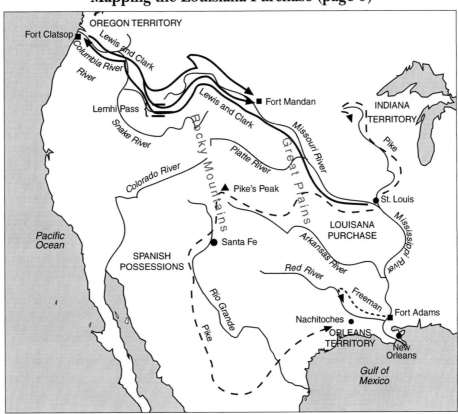

Lewis and Clark (page 7)

Dates of journal entries are given here; students should record details.

1. Rivers: Clark 5/25; Lewis 5/29; Lewis 8/10

2. Native Americans: Lewis 8/19; Clark 8/21

3. Soil and "face of the country": Clark 5/25; Clark 5/31
   Growth and vegetation: Lewis 9/9

4. Animals: Lewis 5/11; Lewis 5/17; Lewis 5/20; Clark 5/29; Lewis 5/27

5. Minerals: Clark 5/25

6. Climate: Lewis 5/30

The War of 1812: Causes (page 10)

Part 1

Tecumseh's confederation, Indian fighting

<u>What</u>: the Shawnee chief Tecumseh put together a confederation of eastern Indians to resist the whites, before the war.

<u>War Cause</u>: Western settlers blamed the British in Canada for urging the Native Americans to fight American whites, although in this case the British were not involved.

British Orders in Council

<u>What</u>: British laws blockading European ports and barring all foreign ships from going to them without first stopping at a British port and paying duties.

<u>War Cause</u>: Angered American shipping interests.

Impressment

<u>What</u>: Great Britain claimed a right to seize British subjects from neutral merchant ships and force them to serve in the British Navy

<u>War Cause</u>: Arrogant British naval officers seized Americans as well as British subjects, and Americans were insulted whenever their ships had to submit to being boarded by British Navy personnel

Crop prices drop

<u>What</u>: Westerners were suffering from a depression in agricultural prices.

<u>War Cause</u>: The westerners blamed the shipping problems caused by the British for their problems, because of a loss of foreign markets.

The *Chesapeake* and *Leopard* encounter

<u>What</u>: The British warship *Leopard* fired on the U.S. frigate *Chesapeake* and impressed some of its crew.

<u>War Cause</u>: Americans were outraged at this clear violation of international law, demanded war.

Western expansion

<u>What</u>: White settlers were continuing to expand into the Northwest Territory.

<u>War Cause</u>: White frontier settlers hoped a victory in war against Great Britain would bring Canadian land to the United States.

Embargo Act of 1807

<u>What</u>: Banned all American exports.

<u>War Cause</u>: Hurt American economy; those affected were bitter and wanted war with Great Britain as a result.

Part 2

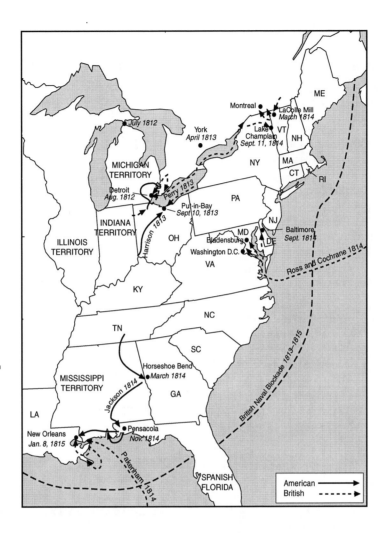

The War of 1812: Yes or No? (page 11)

1. You might support the war because you hope to gain Canadian territory and stop Britain from encouraging Indian hostilities.

2. You might be against the war because you want to keep shipping going, and you are quite certain the U.S. Navy can't prevail against the British Navy.

3. You might favor the war because you think the British interference with U.S. shipping is causing the prices of your crops to fall in New Orleans.

4. You might be against the war because you want to be able to sell your rice abroad, or you might think that winning the war will get rid of the embargo and enable to you ship abroad without interference from Great Britain.

5. You might favor the war, on the British side, because a win might help hold back the tide of white settlers from the United States into your lands.

6. You will probably favor the war to stop impressment.

7. You might favor the war as an extension of the Revolutionary fight against the British, who are once again oppressing your country.

8. You might support the British, hoping to defend your lands against American incursions.

The Monroe Doctrine (page 12)

Part 1

1. European nations are not to create colonies in the Americas from now on.

2. The United States has stayed out of European affairs and will continue to do so.

3. The United States will not interfere with existing European colonies in the Americas. However, the United States will not tolerate any interference by European nations with the newly independent nations of Latin America.

Part 2

Spain: New Spain (Mexico, area that later became U.S. Southwest, Central America)—later Mexico (1821), Central America (1821, then Guatemala, Honduras, Salvador, Nicaragua, and Costa Rica in 1838)
New Granada (northwestern South America)—later Great Columbia (1819), then Colombia, Ecuador, and Venezuela
Peru (western South America), independent in 1824
La Plata (western South America)—then Bolivia (1825), Paraguay (1811), Argentina (Rio de la Plata, 1816), and Chile (1818)
Cuba, Puerto Rico

Great Britain: Jamaica, British Honduras (Belice), British Guiana

France: French Guiana, Haiti

Portugal: Brazil—independent 1822

Netherlands: Dutch Guiana

Manifest Destiny (page 14)

1. *manifest:* obvious, evident

   destiny: fate

   manifest destiny: an outcome that is obviously fated to be

2. Leutze uses stirring images of men, women, and children overcoming obstacles of rugged terrain, injuries, even the trauma of a loved one's death to emerge from shadows to a glorious summit, overlooking a sun-filled horizon of beautiful land stretching into the distance, beckoning to be settled.

3. Providence (fate, God) intends for white Europeans to spread across the entire continent; gives needed expansion room for rapidly multiplying white population; expansion will spread liberty across entire continent, making freedom more secure; English people are natural colonizers, and therefore native Indians are doomed.

The Mexican War: Raising Volunteers (page 16)

<u>Patriotic appeals:</u> New Hampshire as the "strawberry-bed of patriotism"; devotion to country

<u>State pride appeals:</u> New Hampshire as the "strawberry-bed of patriotism" renowned for bravery and devotion to country; "unerring New Hampshire riflemen" and the bravery of her sons

<u>Appeals to prejudice:</u> Santa Anna's "traitor-dagger"; "dastardly meanness and rank toryism of Massachusetts"; "half-civilized Mexicans"

<u>Appeals to manly courage:</u> "bravery"; "fearless and gallant"; "fierce, determined, and undaunted bravery"

<u>Financial appeal:</u> "compensation is $10 per month— $30 in advance. . . . a handsome bounty in money and one hundred and sixty acres of land."

<u>Challenge Question:</u> Tennessee was flooded with volunteers for the war.

The Mexican War: A Chronology Game (page 17)

You may want students to reinforce this page by gluing it to a stiff backing before they cut out the events. You could make this a competition among small groups or among individual students.

Correct chronology, with dates (in order as events appear on activity page):

1824   Mexicans adopt a constitution; Mexico becomes a republic.

1845   Texas joins the Union, becoming the 28th U.S. state.

1847   Mexico City, the capital, falls to U.S. forces led by Winfield Scott.

1821   Stephen Austin leads 300 settlers to Texas from Missouri.

1836   Texas forces led by Sam Houston defeat Santa Anna. Texas becomes a republic, an independent nation.

1848   Mexico and the U.S. sign the Treaty of Guadalupe Hidalgo; the U.S. gains New Mexico and California, plus the Rio Grande boundary line for Texas.

1821   Mexico becomes an independent nation, no longer ruled by Spain.

July 1845   General Zachary Taylor leads U.S. troops into Texas territory that Mexico claims.

1836   Santa Anna's army wipes out American fighters at the Alamo in San Antonio, Texas. Davy Crockett and Jim Bowie die there, along with 200 others.

1500's   Spanish explorers claim Mexico, Texas, and California for Spain.

1846   War starts.

1830   Santa Anna, Mexico's ruler, bans Americans from settling in Texas.

Nov. 1845   U.S. President Polk sends envoy to Mexico, offers to buy Texas, New Mexico, and California (Mexican government refuses to receive the diplomat).

1837   The United States recognizes the new republic of Texas.

The Mexican War: Yes or No? (page 18)

Challenge Question answer: Henry David Thoreau

Mapping the Way West (page 22)

Making Your Own Way West (page 23)

This could be an individual or a small group activity. Suggest that students read actual journals of pioneer travelers first.

After students have created their lists, tell them that when they reach the desert of the Humboldt Sink and/or when they start up the steep mountain passes, the wagons have to be lightened. Students have to begin selecting items that they must discard and leave behind. Every item not absolutely needed for survival must go. What will students select? (You could do this in two stages. First, the wagon is lightened so the exhausted, thirsty oxen can pull it across the waterless Humboldt Sink. Then, the wagon has to be stripped to the utter bare essentials for the trek up and across the rugged Sierra Nevada.)

Mapping Territorial Expansion (page 24)

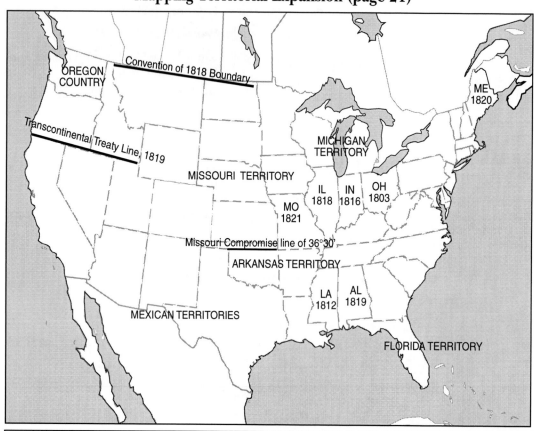

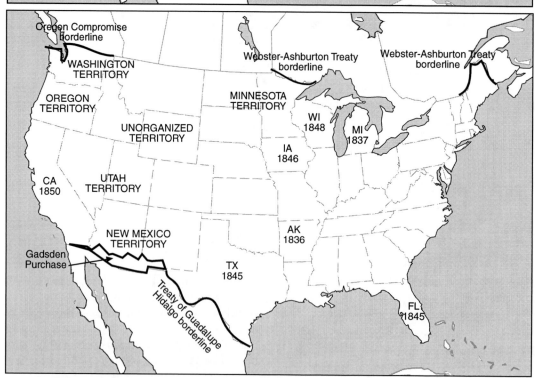

Additional Activity Suggestions

You could have the students do any of the following activities.

1. Read more of Lewis and Clark's journals. (Lewis and Clark were terrible spellers! Rewrite, using correct spelling, some of their more exciting journal entries, like the flash flood near-escape of June 29, 1805, the buffalo run through the camp on May 11, 1805, or the boat upset of May 16, 1805.) Or read the journals of or stories about other explorers and mountain men, like Zebulon Pike, Jedediah Smith, James Beckwourth, and Kit Carson. How were their activities helpful for later settlers?

2. Read a historical novel about the War of 1812. Then rewrite some scenes from the novel from an alternative point of view, such as a young British soldier or a Native American.

3. Create a chart showing the arguments for and against buying Louisiana from France. Or write a strong newspaper or evening television news editorial for or against the purchase.

4. Write two thrilling newspaper accounts of the battle of the Alamo. One is for a U.S. paper; the other is for a Mexican paper.

5. In the first person, describe your experiences as a member of a Mexican ranching family or as a Native American in California as the Anglos began arriving in great numbers, eventually absorbing California into the United States.

6. Create a political brochure for one side of one of the debates.

Unit 1 Assessment

1. Write an essay summarizing the various arguments for and against the United States acquiring the lands west of the Mississippi River. Include specific arguments for and against the Louisiana Purchase, expansion to the Northwest, absorbing Texas as a state, and acquiring territories from Mexico.

2. Trace the events leading up to the War of 1812. Conclude by discussing whether and how the war could have been avoided.

3. Explain why thousands of whites poured west of the Mississippi River during the 1840's. Describe what routes they took and what their trips were typically like.

Unit 2: Native Americans and the Push West

Mapping Native American Removals (page 28)

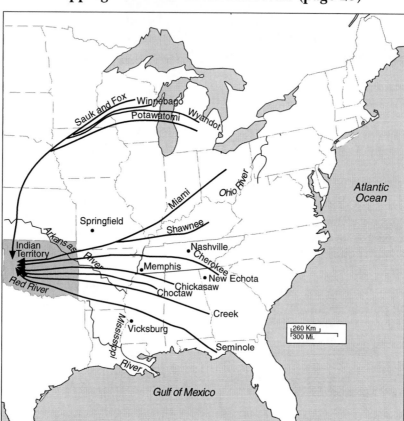

Two Presidents and Their Policies (page 29)

1. Native Americans who depended on hunting as a way of life needed large areas of land to roam in search of game. Native Americans who settled down to farming would need much less land, leaving more for white people and relieving the federal government of having to mediate land conflicts between Indians and whites.

2. Native Americans would build up debts at the government stores; then the government could pressure them to yield land to pay the debts.

3. Jefferson promoted assimilation; Jackson embraced removal of Native Americans to Indian Territory west of the Mississippi River.

4. Jackson claimed the states had a right to control Native American societies within their bounds, which would destroy those distinctive societies. He stated that the claims of the southeastern Indians included lands they didn't actually occupy.

5. Removal of the southeastern Indians would make their traditional lands available for whites. Removal might also end the constant conflicts between whites and Native Americans over land.

6. The lands were not unoccupied and unimproved; Native Americans, especially the Cherokee, cultivated and improved them.

Land Hunger (page 32)

1. Lands taken from Native Americans have always been taken by treaty and purchase (even if the bargain was unfair); using vast areas of land only for hunting, fishing, and gathering is wasteful—Europeans have a right to use land not actually in constant use for their own subsistence; God could not have intended such a beautiful land to remain wild and uncultivated.

Native American Responses—An Activity (page 35)

1. a. Tecumseh, Black Hawk, Osceola

    b. The whites have taken our lands and driven away the game we depend on for food. Our chiefs did not have our permission to sign the treaties giving away our lands. We must not abandon our homes and lands and the ashes of our dead.

2. Red Jacket advocated cultural resistance—do not accept the white people's religion in place of our own.

3. a. Shabonee, Major Ridge

    b. The whites are too numerous and powerful to resist; Native American peoples who attempt to fight the whites will lose everything; removal is our best hope for survival as a nation.

4. The Indians have prior title to the lands, from God, while the whites only have title from the British. The treaties are not valid. (They also pointed out that their lands were settled, cultivated, improved.)

Additional Activity Suggestions

You could have the students do any of the following activities:

1. Read the U.S. Supreme Court rulings in *Cherokee Nation* v. *Georgia* and *Worcester* v. *Georgia*. Summarize the Court's decision in each case. How can the two decisions be logically reconciled?

2. Many Native American peoples greatly admired fine oratory. Find an oration delivered by a Native American leader and deliver it yourself, aloud.

3. Describe the Cherokee way of life in the 1830's just before removal. If they had assimilated thoroughly, living like whites, what was the justification for enforcing the removal policy against them?

4. Attempt to justify logically Andrew Jackson's policy toward South Carolina's nullifiers with his policy about not enforcing the Supreme Court's *Worcester* decision.

Unit 2 Assessment

1. Explain the reasoning behind the federal government policies of Native American assimilation and removal. Was either effective?

2. Create a dialogue among whites and Native Americans on the question of the taking of Indian lands.

Unit 3: The Growing Economy

Inventions and Inventors (page 41)

Thread-spinning mill: Samuel Slater; first step in creating a national textile industry; boosted demand for cotton and factory labor.

Steamboat: Robert Fulton; opened rivers to upstream travel; great boon to shipping, commerce.

Cotton gin: Eli Whitney; much more cotton could now be planted (since it could be de-seeded efficiently); greatly boosted need for slave labor and made most of lower South agricultural.

Telegraph: Samuel F. B. Morse; news and information could now be transmitted immediately; national unifying force.

Metal plow: John Deere; metal blade could cut through prairie sod; made farming the Great Plains efficient.

Mechanical reaper: Cyrus McCormick; farmers could now harvest much more wheat, so they could plant many more acres.

Power loom for mills: Francis Cabot Lowell; second big step in creating fully mechanized textile industry; boosted demand for cotton and cotton clothing; provided factory jobs.

<u>Sewing machine:</u> Elias Howe; ready-made clothing and shoemaking industries now grew rapidly.

<u>Vulcanized rubber:</u> Charles Goodyear; process made rubber strong, elastic, etc.; rubber became an important industrial material.

Getting from Here to There (page 42)

1. <u>steamboat:</u> powered by steam boiler; used to go upstream on rivers, which hadn't been economically possible before; steam boilers would often blow up.

2. <u>clipper ship:</u> used for ocean transport; fastest ships ever, they cut sailing time dramatically, but they had limited cargo space; best for long voyages around South America to California or the Orient, transporting specialty goods.

3. <u>wagon:</u> used on roads to transport heavy, bulky cargo cheaply; could cope with the difficult roads, but shipping by wagon was slow and less efficient than shipping by canal barge or, later, railroad.

4. <u>stagecoach:</u> used mostly to transport people and light, expensive goods and mail; were hard-backed, bumpy, dusty, crowded, uncomfortable, but much faster than walking or wagon travel; small, couldn't carry many people or heavy freight.

5. <u>steam locomotive:</u> used on new railroads to transport people and heavy loads; provides the fastest land transportation yet; efficient; rails open all year; link all parts of the country; steam boilers blew up sometimes.

<u>flatboat:</u> a flat-bottomed boat used to transport people and goods downstream on rivers; it offered cheap transportation (no fuel costs), but it was impractical to take upstream.

<u>canal barge:</u> used on the many canals constructed in the 1800's; pulled by horses on a towpath next to the canal; canals were expensive to create, but shipping on canal barges was much cheaper, smoother, and quicker than transporting heavy goods on roads; canals sometimes froze in winter.

<u>iron steamship:</u> used for ocean transport of cargo; slower than clipper ships in favorable winds, but on the average faster and had much greater cargo space than clippers and other wooden ships and was also stronger and cheaper to maintain; made transatlantic shipping cheaper, and brought emigrants back to U.S. cheaply on the return trip.

Mapping the New Travel Routes (page 44)

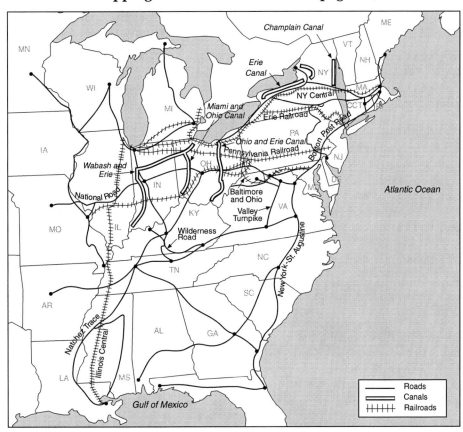

The Industrial Revolution and You (page 48)

Answers will vary. Possible responses:

1. You go to work at the Lowell Mills for an interesting change of pace and to earn some money.

2. Your hand weaving is no longer needed; you go to work in a textile mill.

3. You are able to grow a lot more wheat using the Deere plow and the McCormick reaper, and you can get your wheat to market with the new transportation options.

4. You may be "sold South" to meet the demand in the lower South for more slaves to work the expanding cotton lands.

5. You go to work in a mill or other factory, and you live in a dark, crowded tenement.

6. Demand for your services drops sharply after Eli Whitney starts producing guns with interchangeable parts.

7. You were struggling economically until Whitney invented the cotton gin; now you are expanding your plantation, growing many more acres of cotton and adding many more slaves.

8. You purchase some of the new industrial sewing machines and expand your business dramatically.

Reading the Immigration Graph (page 50)

1. a. No; it dropped occasionally (between 1836 and 1838; 1842 and 1844; after 1854).

    b. Yes (from approximately 8,500 to about 430,000).

2. The disruptions of the Napoleonic wars ended.

3. a. From 1836 to 1838.

   b. Maybe the Panic of 1837.

4. a. After 1854.

   b. The Irish escaping the potato blight and Europeans fleeing the failed revolutions had come in a rush after 1848; conditions were now more stable in Europe.

5. a. Just over 100%.

   b. After the Irish potato blight hit, Irish people began starving. The choice was immigration or death.

6. a. The U.S. Civil War began.

   b. The war had ended by 1866.

Additional Activity Suggestions

You could have the students do any of the following activities.

1. Describe the reasons why people from nations other than Ireland chose to emigrate to the United States—for example, Germans, Chinese, Britons, and Scandinavians. Where did these people tend to settle? What types of occupations did they tend to pursue?

2. Create a time line of the industrial revolution—inventions, technological advances, transportation changes and routes, urban and immigration growth, Supreme Court decisions favoring the market economy, labor strikes, and so on.

3. Compare city life in the 1840's with city life today. Show differences and similarities through pictures, contemporary descriptions, and historical records. Use a chart to compare aspects of life such as jobs, housing, public services, health, education, and ethnic, racial, and religious tensions.

4. Create a graph that shows how cities grew rapidly during the industrial revolution era. Show on a map how these cities were distributed geographically.

5. Write a narrative or a dramatic interpretation about the labor conflict in the antebellum period. Show perspectives of workers and employers, and divisions among the laboring classes.

Unit 3 Assessment

1. Write an essay discussing how the industrial revolution changed life for everyday Americans.

2. Discuss the ways in which the industrial revolution was different in the North, South, and West of the United States.

3. Discuss the impact on the nation of the wave of immigration in the 1830's and 1840's.

Unit 4: African-Americans and the Growth of Slavery

Graphing Slavery (page 56)

Approximate white/black percentages:

Massachusetts: White 99%; Black 1%

Pennsylvania: White 98% (97.66%); Black 2% (2.33%)

Ohio: White 98.7%; Black 1.3%

Virginia: White 63%; Black 37%

South Carolina: White 41%; Black 59%

Forms of Resistance (page 60)

Answers will vary somewhat. Some samples:

faking illness and injury; stealing and pilfering; abusing elderly or ill owners; working slowly; doing clumsy, poor work; damaging crops, tools, etc., "by accident"; pretending to be stupid, unable to understand what you're ordered to do; slipping away at night to secret religious meetings; making up and singing songs with hidden resistance and/or escape meanings

Slavery Time Line (page 61)

Time line dates:

1793   Fugitive Slave Law

1793   invention of the cotton gin

1794   first convention of abolition societies

1800   Gabriel Prosser's revolt

1807   importation of slaves into the U.S. forbidden

1816   American Colonization Society founded

1820   Missouri Compromise

1822   Liberia founded

1822   Denmark Vesey's revolt

1827   *Freedom's Journal* starts publishing

1831   Nat Turner's revolt

1831   *The Liberator* starts publishing

1832-33   various antislavery societies are founded

1834-35   mob violence against blacks and abolition breaks out

1837   Elijah Lovejoy is killed

1839   the *Amistad* revolt

1841   Douglass makes his first antislavery speech

1841   the *Creole* revolt

1848   Free Soil party is formed

1850   Compromise of 1850

1852   *Uncle Tom's Cabin* is published in book form

1854   Kansas-Nebraska Act

1854   Republican party is formed

1857   Dred Scott decision

1859   John Brown's raid

If students have completed the "Slavery Time Line" activity in Unit 7 of Book 2 of this series, they can add these items to that time line.

Secret Messages (page 62)

1. a. Tells about the enslavement of the Israelites in Egypt under the Pharaoh, and Moses leading them out of Egypt to the Promised Land.

   b. They intend to leave their land of slavery for freedom in the North, just as the Israelites left Egypt.

   c. "Moses" was the nickname of Harriet Tubman, who got her nickname from leading hundreds of her people from slavery in the South to freedom in the North.

2. Escape from slavery; also, a code message that there will be a religious or other meeting in the woods that night.

3. a. The Jordan is a great river in the Middle East often mentioned in the Bible.

   b. They are referring to the Ohio River, the great dividing line between slave and free states, the last barrier runaway slaves must overcome to reach northern territory.

4. a. The constellation called the Big Dipper .

   b. The Big Dipper pointed the way North for escaping slaves to follow at night.

Free Blacks in the North (page 64)

1. <u>death:</u> cemeteries are racially segregated (not all actually were).

2. <u>education:</u> northern schools are segregated (not all actually were).

3. <u>entertainment:</u> blacks can't purchase good seats, where the whites sit.

4. <u>legal system:</u> judges are all white, so lawsuits or other legal challenges by blacks don't receive a fair hearing; prejudice prevents them from serving as jurors even though they're legally entitled to do so.

5. <u>medical care:</u> hospitals are segregated.

6. <u>religion:</u> blacks have to worship in their own churches with black clergy, not in white churches (actually, they were sometimes allowed to attend white churches, but they had separate and inferior seating).

7. <u>voting:</u> blacks are threatened with violence if they vote, which they are legally entitled to do (soon, northern states would take away this legal right for free blacks to vote).

Additional Activity Suggestions

You could have the students do any of the following activities.

1. Write a first-person description of a slave uprising, like the ones of Gabriel Prosser, Denmark Vesey, or Nat Turner.

2. Find out how free African-Americans like Richard Allen and Absalom Jones worked to make social conditions in the North more equal for their fellow blacks.

3. Present a skit, a one-act play, or a dramatic reading of an escape from slavery via the Underground Railroad.

4. Create a graph showing the relationship of the growth of cotton production and the growth of the slave population in the South.

5. Draw a site plan of a typical southern plantation. On the plan, or on a separate chart, note the roles and responsibilities of different classes and genders of people on the plantation.

6. Draw some routes on a map tracing slaves' escape journeys. How many miles did slaves from different states have to travel to reach free soil (north or south)?

Unit 4 Assessment

1. Write an essay describing the effects of Eli Whitney's invention of the cotton gin on life in the South.

2. Describe the various ways African-Americans coped with life under slavery.

3. The "Slave Voices" activity would be a good assessment vehicle.

Unit 5: Politics

Answer to question on Student Background Pages: The United States had three presidents in the year 1841. Martin Van Buren was president for the first few months, until William Harrison's inauguration; Harrison died a month after his inauguration, when John Tyler became president.

Political Cartoons (page 69)

1. Jackson often used the veto to strike down laws passed by Congress that he didn't like; he increased the power of the executive branch of the government; he also refused to enforce some Supreme Court rulings he disagreed with.

2. Jackson is dressed in the sumptuous robes of a king, and he wears a crown and holds a scepter; he is trampling on the Constitution of the United States, the judiciary of the United States, and congressional measures such as appropriations for internal improvements (roads, canals, etc.) and the U.S. Bank.

3. Jackson was simply acting in the best interests of the people of the United States, who had elected him; he had a right to use his veto power; Congress could always override his vetoes if his opponents could muster enough votes.

Political Parties and the Issues (page 71)

Slavery: This issue divided along sectional rather than party lines.
Democrats: the party included both supporters and opponents of slavery.
Whigs: also divided.

Central government versus state powers
Democrats: middle of the road—national power should be kept within close limits; states' righters liked this party, but Jackson was strongly against nullification.
Whigs: favored strong national government to check too much individualism in politics; however, disliked an extremely strong president.

The economy
Democrats: no national bank, anti big business, for free and open economic opportunity.
Whigs: for a national bank and national guidance of the economy.

Immigrants
Democrats: embraced the worth of the "small" or "common man," which included immigrants.
Whigs: distrusted and disliked excess participation in politics of rough, uneducated, poor, and otherwise nonaristocratic people, which most of the immigrants were.

Democracy
Democrats: favored participation by common people in government, both in voting and in office holding; any common person could perform any public office.
Whigs: favored leadership and office by better-educated, more economically advantaged people.

The spoils system
Democrats: started it in a big way under Jackson.
Whigs: complained loudly about it under Jackson, but practiced it themselves when they got into office.

Extra Challenge

1. <u>National Republican:</u> opposition to Jackson/ for the national bank.

2. <u>Free Soil:</u> no slavery, especially in the territories.

3. <u>American (Know-Nothing):</u> opposition to immigrants and Catholics.

4. <u>Liberty:</u> abolition of slavery.

A Gallery of Presidents (page 72)

1. James Madison (1809–1817)
2. Andrew Jackson (1829–1837)
3. Zachary Taylor (1849–1850)
4. William H. Harrison (1841)
5. Thomas Jefferson (1801–1809)
6. James K. Polk (1845–1849)
7. James Monroe (1817–1825)
8. Franklin Pierce (1853–1857)
9. Martin Van Buren (1837–1841)
10. James Buchanan (1857–1861)
11. John Tyler (1841–1845)
12. John Quincy Adams (1825–1829)
13. Millard Fillmore (1850–1853)

The Slavery Issue (page 75)

<u>Northwest Ordinance (1787):</u> Banned slavery from the Northwest Territories.

<u>Three-Fifths Compromise (1787):</u> Agreement at the Constitutional Convention between free and slave states that three fifths of slaves would be counted when calculating the number of a state's representatives in the House.

<u>Missouri Compromise (1820):</u> Agreement to admit Missouri as a slave state and Maine as a free state at the same time, and also to ban slavery in the rest of the Louisiana Purchase territory.

<u>Nullification Crisis (1832–33):</u> Face-off when South Carolina claimed a right to nullify the new tariff passed by Congress so it could claim the same right if laws abolishing slavery were passed.

<u>Wilmot Proviso (1846):</u> Proviso passed by the House of Representatives banning slavery in territories acquired from Mexico.

<u>Admission of Oregon (1848):</u> Slavery was banned here.

<u>Compromise of 1850:</u> The compromise that temporarily saved the Union; North and South agreed on a series of measures, admitting California as a free state; other territories to decide themselves on slavery; no slave trade in D.C.; strong fugitive slave law.

<u>Fugitive Slave Act of 1850:</u> New, strong law to be enforced in the North; caused much agitation there.

Regions and Issues (page 79)

<u>Protective tariff</u>
North: Manufacturers favored it, except that New England shipping interests were for free trade.
South: Favored it at first, hoping to develop industry; then turned against it, as their economy was based on exports and they needed to buy many imported goods.
West: Divided, depending on whether an area had products to protect.

<u>Sale of western lands</u>
North: Favored getting a good price for these lands, so cheap labor wouldn't all flock to the West.
South: Favored getting a good price for the lands, so Southwest wouldn't open up huge new cotton-growing competition.
West: Favored low prices to promote continued development and settlement.

<u>Internal improvements</u>
North: Favored federal support to benefit its industry and commerce.
South: Got few benefits from this (most roads, canals, and railroads were built or improved in the North and West).

West: Favored federal support to benefit its farmers, so they could ship produce.

National bank
    North: Mildly opposed to particular proposals.
    South: Mildly favored.
    West: Mildly favored, until the Panic of 1819 produced opposition.

Slavery (the most divisive issue)
    North: Against.
    South: For.
    West: Tended toward support (some Southwest states were slave; other western states had many settlers originally from the South).

Nullification
    North: Opposed, because the northern states favored laws and policies the South wanted to nullify.
    South: Favored, so southern states could nullify any possible antislavery laws, as well as unfavorable tariff laws.
    West: Divided, tended to be opposed for same reasons as the North.

Additional Activity Suggestions

You could have the students do any of the following activities:

1. Find examples of other political cartoons from the 1820's, 1830's, or 1840's. Make a class display of these. Note the symbols used in each, and explain the point the cartoonist is making.

2. Presidents weren't the only important political leaders in the antebellum period. In fact, some men in Congress were just as—or more—powerful and influential. Create a class display showcasing such outstanding figures as Daniel Webster, John C. Calhoun, and Henry Clay. Include pictures of each man, brief biographies, interesting quotes of the man's own words, and a summary of the important roles they played in their times.

3. Explain how and why states, at the same time they were granting the vote to all white males, were also taking the vote away from free black males.

4. Write a lively first-person account of your experiences at Andrew Jackson's first inaugural.

5. Compare an antebellum presidential campaign with a recent one. Compare things such as campaigning style, use of slogans, efforts to get out the vote, and addressing or avoiding the issues.

Assessment

1. Write an essay describing how American political life changed during the Jacksonian era.

2. Write political brochures for each major political party during one of the antebellum presidential election campaigns.

3. The "Slavery West of the Mississippi" activity would make an effective assessment vehicle.

Unit 6: Reform Movements and the National Culture

Abolition Plans (page 84)

1. Colonization was best because blacks and whites cannot live together peaceably—whites are prejudiced, blacks resent the abuses of slavery, and there are distinctions "which nature has made."

2. Garrison wanted immediate abolition. Tallmadge advocated gradual abolition (somehow).

3. These people thought that slavery would eventually fall by itself, inevitably.

4. Walker's approach was most radical—blacks would take up arms and free themselves. Black slaves did sometimes rise together, as in the Prosser, Vesey, and Turner revolts.

Women's Grievances (page 88)

You could have students do this as a small group activity, or you could go over each grievance, one by one, in class, developing the list, to help students who may find the language and syntax especially challenging.

Political Wrongs: Can't vote; have to obey laws they have no voice in forming; if single, must pay taxes although they can't vote.

Social Wrongs: Can't go to college; can't be a minister or take part in church affairs; men hold them to a different moral standard and tell them what their sphere in society is, keeping them dependent.

Legal Wrongs: If married, have no legal rights (can't control their property or keep their earnings); must obey husbands, who can beat them; divorce laws favor men.

Economic Wrongs: They are banned from profitable jobs; paid low wages.

An Age of Reform (page 90)

Dorothea Dix: i

Thomas Gallaudet: e

Elizabeth Cady Stanton: j, b

Charles G. Finney: c

Neal Dow: f

William Lloyd Garrison: j

Lyman Beecher: c, f

Sarah and Angela Grimké: j, b

Horace Mann: h

Dr. Samuel Gridley Howe: a

Robert Owen: g

Susan B. Anthony: j, b

Amelia Bloomer: d

Frederick Douglass: j

Mary Lyon: k

Lucretia Mott: j, b

Challenge Question: Women who worked in the abolition movement often were inspired by this to become active in the new movement for women's rights.

American Writers (page 91)

A whale of a tale: *Moby Dick,* by Herman Melville

Life in the woods: *Walden,* by Henry David Thoreau

The last of the tribe: *The Last of the Mohicans,* by James Fenimore Cooper

Yesterday's Stephen King: Edgar Allan Poe (with a title of one of his short stories)

Red alphabet: *The Scarlet Letter,* by Nathaniel Hawthorne

Green poetry: *Leaves of Grass,* by Walt Whitman

Native American "tune": *The Song of Hiawatha,* by Henry Wadsworth Longfellow

A really long nap: "Rip Van Winkle," by Washington Irving

Additional Activity Suggestions

You could have the students do any of the following activities:

1. Develop a class display of works by nineteenth-century artists such as George Catlin, William Sidney Mount, George Caleb Bingham, Thomas Doughty, Thomas Cole, and Asher B. Durand.

2. Draw up a modern-day list of grievances patterned after the list in the Seneca Falls Declaration of Sentiments. Do female and male students have different points of view on this?

3. The Seneca Falls Declaration said, "In entering upon the great work before us, we anticipate no small amount of misconception, misrepresentation, and ridicule; but we shall use every instrumentality within our power to effect our object." How does this apply to the feminist movement of the 1970's and later?

4. The Seneca Falls Declaration ends with 12 resolutions. They are objectives for women to achieve. Find a copy of the Declaration and read these resolutions. To what extent have American women achieved these objectives today?

5. Deliver a fiery abolitionist speech.

6. Create a chart comparing the major utopian communities of the antebellum period, such as the Rappites, the Amana Community, the Shakers, the Oneida Community, Fourierist colonies, and New Harmony.

Unit 6 Assessment

1. The "Abolition Plans" and "The Proslavery Response" role-play would be effective assessment vehicles for the abolition movement.

2. Discuss the interrelationship between the abolition and women's rights movements.

ADDITIONAL RESOURCES

Historical Fiction for Students

Baker, Betty. *The Dunderhead War* (Mexican-American War).

Blos, Joan. *A Gathering of Days: A New England Girl's Journal, 1830–1832* (Newbery Medal winner).

Bohner, Charles. *Bold Journey: West with Lewis and Clark*.

Brenner, Barbara. *On the Frontier with Mr. Audubon* (boy travels with Audubon).

Fox, Paula. *The Slave Dancer* (kidnapped white boy aboard a slave ship).

Fritz, Jean. *Brady* (Underground Railroad).

Humphrey, William. *No Resting Place* (Cherokee removal).

Lasky, Kathryn. *Beyond the Divide* (pioneer journey).

Lord, Athena V. *A Spirit to Ride the Whirlwind* (the Lowell mill workers).

Lyons, Mary E. *Letters from a Slave Girl: The Story of Harriet Jacobs* (based on Jacobs's autobiography).

Morrow, Honore. *On to Oregon!* (pioneer journey).

Murrow, Liza Ketchum. *West Against the Wind* (pioneer journey).

O'Dell, Scott. *Streams to the River, River to the Sea: A Novel of Sacagawea*.

Parker, T. M. *The Far Battleground* (Mexican-American War).

Paulsen, Gary. *Nightjohn* (harsh realities of slave life).

Smucker, Barbara. *Runaway to Freedom* (Underground Railroad).

Wallin, Luke. *In the Shadow of Wind* (white boy and Creeks).

Nonfiction for Students

Bealer, Alex. *Only the Names Remain: The Cherokee and the Trail of Tears*.

Lester, Julius. *To Be a Slave*.

Macaulay, David. *Mill*.

Mellon, James, ed. *Bullwhip Days: The Slaves Remember—An Oral History*.

Meltzer, Milton. *Andrew Jackson and His America*.

_____, ed. *In Their Own Words: A History of the American Negro 1619–1865*.

Nabokov, Peter, ed. *Native American Testimony: A Chronicle of Indian-White Relations from Prophecy to the Present, 1492–1992*.

The Old West. Time-Life Books (20+ volumes).

Selden, Bernice. *The Mill Girls: Lucy Larcom, Harriet Hanson Robinson, and Sarah G. Bagley*.

Vogel, Virgil J., ed. *This Country Was Ours: A Documentary History of the American Indian*.

Collections of Primary Source Documents: Print

The Annals of America. Chicago: Encyclopedia Britannica, 1968.

Vol. 4 1797–1820: Domestic Expansion and Foreign Entanglements.

Vol. 5 1821–1832: Steps Toward Equalitarianism.

Vol. 6 1833–1840: The Challenge of a Continent.

Vol. 7 1841–1849: Manifest Destiny.

Commager, Henry Steele, ed. *Documents of American History*, 9th ed. (2 vols.). Englewood Cliffs, NJ: Prentice-Hall, 1973.

Craven, Avery, Walter Johnson, and F. Roger Dunn. *A Documentary History of the American People.* Boston: Ginn and Company, 1951.

Hart, Albert Bushnell. *American History as Told by Contemporaries.* New York: The Macmillan Company, 1901.

  Vol. III: National Expansion 1783–1845.

  Vol. IV: Welding of the Nation 1845–1900.

Historical Statistics of the United States. Washington, DC: U.S. Department of Commerce, Bureau of the Census, 1975.

Miller, Marion Mills, ed. *Great Debates in American History.* New York: Current Literature Publishing Company, 1913 (14 volumes in all).

  Vol. II: Foreign Relations, Part 1.

  Vol. IV: Slavery from 1790 to 1857.

CD-ROM

America Adventure. Knowledge Adventure (also available as a DOS floppy disk).

American Indian 2.0. Facts On File.

American Journey—History in Your Hands. Research Publications.

  The African-American Experience

  Westward Expansion

  Women in America

CD Sourcebook of American History. InfoBases.

500 Nations. Microsoft.

Landmark Documents in American History. Facts On File (dwarfs the print collections).

Oregon Trail II. MECC (updated version).

World Wide Web/Internet

Sites with Numerous Links to U.S. History Sources:

Government/Social Studies Sources (includes listings of Library of Congress exhibits, historical documents from Project Gutenburg, other social studies Web sites): http://www.nwoca.ohio.gov/www/gov.html

History/Social Studies Web Site for K–12 Teachers (includes site map, What's New Archive, sources arranged by category): http://www.execpc.com/~dboals/boals.html

Library of Congress home page (includes American Memory historical collections): http://lcweb.loc.gov

Kathy Schrock's site (a Cape Cod teacher's excellent list of resources): http://www.capecod.net/schrockguide

U.S. Historic Documents (primary documents in full text): http://www.ukans.edu/carrie/docs/amdocs_index.html

GLOSSARY

abolition—putting an end to something, wiping it out; the abolition movement, or **abolitionism**, wanted to end (abolish) slavery in the United States.

antebellum—pre-Civil War.

assimilation—federal policy of trying to persuade Native Americans to adopt white ways and become part of the mainstream culture.

compromise—an agreement where each side gives in on some points; also, to come to such an agreement.

cotton gin—a machine invented by Eli Whitney that removed seeds from cotton bolls efficiently.

emigrant—person who leaves her or his native country for life in a different country.

fugitive—runaway.

immigration—people coming into a country that they are not natives of, intending to live there permanently.

impressment—British practice of taking sailors off U.S. ships and forcing them to serve in the British Royal Navy.

industrial revolution—the rapid change in the U.S. economy toward production in factories using power machinery.

"internal" slave trade—the trade that sold slaves from the upper South to the lower South to provide the labor needed on expanding cotton plantations.

manifest destiny—the idea that the United States was obviously fated to expand all the way west to the Pacific Ocean.

nullify—to declare a law void, having no legal effect; **nullification** is the act of nullifying.

orator—a person admired for his or her skill and power in public speaking; an **oration** is an elaborate speech delivered formally and with dignity.

plantation—a large, self-sufficient farm, much like a miniature village of its own; common in the antebellum South.

popular sovereignty—allowing the people in each territory to decide for or against slavery there themselves.

proviso—an article or clause introducing something.

removal—federal policy of removing eastern Indians from their traditional lands and resettling them west of the Mississippi River.

secede—to withdraw from, as in a state *seceding* from the Union; **secession** is the act of seceding.

tariff—a set of taxes on goods brought into one country from another country.

textile—cloth.

Underground Railroad—the network of people who helped runaway slaves escape to the North and to Canada.

Notes

Share Your Bright Ideas with Us!

We want to hear from you! Your valuable comments and suggestions will help us meet your current and future classroom needs.

Your name_____Date_____

School name_____Phone_____

School address_____

Grade level taught_____Subject area(s) taught_____Average class size_____

Where did you purchase this publication?_____

Was your salesperson knowledgeable about this product?   Yes_____   No_____

What monies were used to purchase this product?

___School supplemental budget   ___Federal/state funding   ___Personal

Please "grade" this Walch publication according to the following criteria:

Quality of service you received when purchasing ....A   B   C   D   F
Ease of use...A   B   C   D   F
Quality of content..A   B   C   D   F
Page layout ....A   B   C   D   F
Organization of material ....A   B   C   D   F
Suitability for grade level..A   B   C   D   F
Instructional value...A   B   C   D   F

COMMENTS:_____

_____

What specific supplemental materials would help you meet your current—or future—instructional needs?

_____

Have you used other Walch publications? If so, which ones?_____

May we use your comments in upcoming communications?   ___Yes   ___No

Please **FAX** this completed form to **207-772-3105**, or mail it to:

Product Development, J.Weston Walch, Publisher, P.O. Box 658, Portland, ME 04104-0658

We will send you a **FREE GIFT** as our way of thanking you for your feedback.   **THANK YOU!**